Eat Yourself Healthy

The Recipe for Scotland's Health

Eat Yourself Healthy

The Recipe for Scotland's Health

Debbie Dalrymple

Scottish Consumer Council

EDINBURGH: THE STATIONERY OFFICE

The Stationery Office Limited
South Gyle Crescent, Edinburgh EH12 9EB

First Published 1997

British Library Cataloguing in Publications Data

A catalogue record for this book is available from the British Library

ISBN 0 11 495838 6

Illustrations by Yvonne Holton

Contents

About the Scottish Consumer Council

The Scottish Consumer Council (SCC) was set up by the government in 1975 and aims to promote the interests of Scottish consumers, with particular regard to those people who experience disadvantages in society.

The SCC has no statutory powers and relies on careful research and persuasive lobbying.

Although funded mainly by the Government through a grant-in-aid from the Department of Trade and Industry, the SCC is independent of any political party and critically assesses the policies of successive governments using the consumer principles of access, choice, information, safety, redress and representation.

The Council carries out research into the policies and practices of local government, business, industry and the professions and lobbies these bodies, when justified, to improve their services to the consumer.

The work for this book was overseen by the SCC's Food, Diet and Environment Committee.

The SCC is grateful for the assistance of Linda Maher and Gordon Campbell.

The SCC gratefully acknowledges the financial assistance of Safeway plc.

SCOTTISH CONSUMER COUNCIL

Scottish Consumer Council, Royal Exchange House,
100 Queen Street, Glasgow, G1 3DN

Foreword

The shortcomings of the Scottish diet have undoubtedly contributed to a number of our major long-term health problems, including coronary heart disease, some forms of cancer and diseases such as diabetes. As Chief Medical Officer for Scotland, I welcome the initiative taken by the Scottish Consumer Council to produce this excellent book *Eat Yourself Healthy*. The book gives renewed emphasis to the importance of healthy eating and complements the information provided by The Scottish Office in its Diet Action Plan, 'Eating for Health', which was published last year.

I am particularly impressed by the readable, commonsense approach adopted by Debbie Dalrymple and the Scottish Consumer Council. They have avoided oversimplification but at the same time have managed to make a potentially confusing subject sound quite straightforward. Useful practical advice is presented in the sections entitled 'Healthy Shopping' and 'Healthy Cooking Techniques', and I am confident that the 28-day plan of recipes will prove of immense value.

I would like to reinforce the message that we must all buy food which provides a healthy, balanced diet and which represents good value for money. We should heed the advice to buy fresh food whenever possible and to become discerning shoppers, looking critically at the content of calories, fat and sugar of the packaged foods that we purchase.

All of the people of Scotland can benefit from this book. It represents a further important step towards improving the health of our nation and I commend it to you unreservedly.

Sir David Carter
Chief Medical Officer for Scotland

Introduction

The Scots are well known for their 'sweet tooth'. We are fond of confectionery, cakes, biscuits and fizzy drinks. We are also a little too fond of deep-fried foods, pies, chips and crisps, and we do not eat enough fruit and vegetables.

It has now emerged through research that our preference for the sugary and fatty, or rather *the proportion* of these things within our everyday diet, pushes Scotland to the bottom of the health league tables. We have one of the least healthy diets in the Western world. The grim fact is, a poor diet can eventually lead to serious illness.

But it is never too late to change what you eat, and even small changes can help you enjoy a healthier future. Foods which contain fats or sugar are not harmful in themselves. Eaten in moderation as part of a balanced diet, they're perfectly all right. What counts is the word 'balanced'. A balanced and nutritious diet is good for your health and well-being. Eating well is a long-term investment in staying well.

So, to help propel Scotland into the premier league in the health tables, nutrition experts, food professionals and The Scottish Office have together agreed that there are key changes most of us need to make, and have drawn up some dietary targets for us for the year 2005. Findings show that typical Scottish eating is low in fruit, vegetables and cereal. At the same time it is high in confectionery, sweet and salty snacks, sugary drinks and products containing high fat. So we have to look at alternatives.

Alternative diet? Healthy foods? Sounds costly?

Well, no it's not. As *Eat Yourself Healthy* shows, a healthy diet does not necessarily require expensive food. By following these simple ideas and guidelines you will find that changing your current eating habits is neither expensive nor difficult. And on top of that, you'll find your new menus more exciting and more fun.

Eating yourself healthy means:

- having a wide variety of foods – it does not mean giving up your favourites, nor does it mean spending more money on food

- eating more fruit and vegetables, breads, cereals, pasta, rice and potatoes
- cutting down on foods which are high in fat, salt and sugar.

In *Eat Yourself Healthy* we have carefully translated Scotland's dietary targets into menu ideas. By setting out new and exciting menus to cover a 28-day eating plan, we demonstrate how easy it can be to change to a tasty and varied diet that is healthy too.

And preparation?

You'll discover our recipes are simple, quick to make and have been put together with a careful eye on cost. You may find some of the ingredients unfamiliar, but they can be bought in most supermarkets, and in many cases we suggest other options should items be difficult to find. Also included are handy tips to help form the basis of a healthy eating lifestyle.

Here in Scotland we have some of the highest quality home-grown food produce available, and supermarkets now stock a huge variety of fresh fruit and vegetables all year round. There's therefore plenty of choice in healthy and inexpensive ingredients. All this has been taken into account in compiling this book, together with the trend towards eating more international foods. It means traditional Scottish recipes feature alongside more contemporary suggestions – curries and pastas, for instance. Even some old favourites have been modified to give healthier alternatives.

The result is a broad-ranging, contrasting and informative recipe book, generously peppered with tips and suggestions to make healthy eating a more exciting and more appetising way of life.

So read on, and enjoy!

The Balance of Good Health

A balanced diet is essential for our bodies to work properly and keep us in good health. A mixture of foods will make sure we get all the required nutrients. There are five basic food groups:

- fruit and vegetables
- bread, other cereals and potatoes
- milk and dairy foods
- meat, fish and alternatives
- foods containing fat, and foods containing sugar.

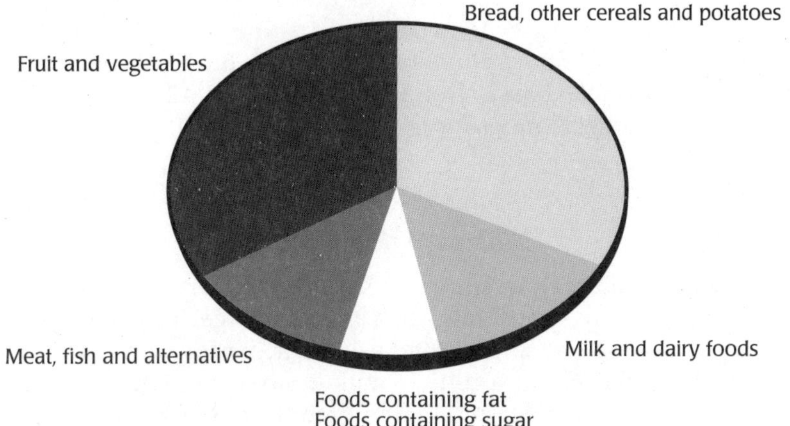

This chart helps to show the amounts of food type that we should eat as part of a balanced diet. The following points help to summarise this information, and should become part of our daily eating habits. But don't expect to make all these changes at once. Even if you start by taking just small steps, you will begin to feel better straightaway. The important thing is to start.

Fruit and vegetables

Aim for five portions a day

This includes fruit such as oranges, bananas and apples taken as snacks, and vegetables and salads that are served with meals. Why not try sticks of carrot, celery and cucumber rather than crisps when you fancy a snack? A glass of fruit juice, such as orange juice or grapefuit juice, is a good way to start the day. Use any kind of fruit and vegetables, including fresh, frozen, tinned, dried, and pure, unsweetened fruit juices. Make sure that tinned fruits are in fruit juice and not syrup.

Bread, cereals and potatoes

Aim for six slices of bread a day

Eat plenty of starchy foods like bread, cereals, pasta, rice, beans and pulses. Try to make sure that they contain as much of their natural fibre as possible, like brown breads, brown rice and wholemeal pasta. Don't be tempted to add too much butter or rich, creamy sauces.

Milk and dairy foods

Where possible, choose the low-fat types of dairy produce and avoid too many 'hard' fats, such as lard, margarine and butter. Try to use low-fat spreads and use them sparingly in cooking. Drinking about half a pint of milk a day (skimmed or semi-skimmed and whole milk for children) is good for you.

Meat, fish and protein alternatives

Aim to eat fish two or three times a week

Small portions of foods such as chicken, fish, meat, eggs, beans and lentils give you the protein you need to make up a balanced diet. Try to eat oil-rich fish, such as sardines, herring, mackerel, salmon and tuna. Trim or drain the excess fat off meat.

Foods containing fat, and foods containing sugar

Cut down on sugary foods and drinks. Try to cut out sugar in tea and coffee, and avoid sprinkling sugar on to food. Make sweets and cakes a special treat instead of an everyday item. If you only buy them now and again instead of keeping them in the house, they'll be a lot easier to resist. Try to use more vegetable-based oils and spreads, such as sunflower or olive oil.

HEALTHY HINTS

Side salads

Salads are a good way of ensuring that we eat lots of fruit and vegetables that have the nutrients, vitamins and fibre that we need in our diets. Try the following ingredients in your salads and make up combinations that you like: lettuce, cucumber, cabbage, carrot, tomato, radish, courgette, onions, lentils, peppers, broccoli, oranges, apples, apricots, spinach, peas and sweetcorn.

Bread

Try to serve bread with every meal. If it's brown even better. Eat it with soup, have it toasted for a snack and use it to mop up sauces and gravies. But go easy on the butter and fatty spreads. Don't use them at all if possible. Wholemeal breads taste so good you won't need to add anything.

Fruit

Keep your fruit bowl well stocked and in a prominent position so that your family remember to snack healthily. Keep dried fruits such as apricots, prunes and sultanas in the store cupboard so that you reach for them instead of crisps and biscuits.

Vegetables

Try to cook vegetables as close to the date of purchase as possible and don't over-cook them as they will lose more of their nutritional value. Frozen vegetables are best cooked from frozen rather than being allowed to defrost before cooking.

Healthy Shopping

To help to change the way you eat, you can make a start by adapting your approach to shopping and cooking. Think 'balanced diet'. Old habits may seem difficult to break – loading up the supermarket trolley with chocolate biscuits, crisps and cakes – but remember these items only provide 'empty calories'. They don't give you much nutritional benefit and, if the energy they contain is more than you need, it will be stored as body fat. So limit the amount you eat, and use them as occasional treats only. If you start shopping with more awareness, this will help keep temptation at bay.

When shopping, the aim should be two-fold:

- to buy food that contributes towards a healthy balanced diet
- to buy food that represents good value for money.

Try to buy fresh foods wherever possible. Look for seasonal fruits and vegetables and special offers on food. As you become more confident in cooking, it will become easier to shop for good value bargains. Surprisingly quickly you'll become adept at putting together your own recipes based on what is available, fresh and good value.

Another valuable tip. Always look at food labelling to see what is actually in the food you're buying. Be aware not only of the total calories, but also of the fat and sugar content.

Many people worry that a healthy diet will cost them more money. Certainly if you rush out and spend a lot on new ingredients for a meal you only make once then you will be out of pocket. However, if you follow the basic message of only making small changes here and there to your diet, then it should not have to cost you more. And remember: you may be buying less of some items to balance out buying more of others. Eating more bread will be cheaper than buying snack foods, and pulses and pasta are cheaper than meat. You can also make a lot of changes to your own diet without having to rely on the healthy-option products promoted by all the major manufacturers and retailers.

Remember the basic tips for improving your diet:

Eat more fresh fruit and vegetables

Serve a side salad with meals

Eat more bread, potatoes, pulses, pasta and rice

Eat more fish, especially oil-rich varieties

Moderate meat intake

Moderate salt and sugar intake, and particulary saturated fat such as butter and cream

- **Use herbs and spices to season instead of salt**

Reduce fat intake

- **Try low-fat options**
- **Remove or drain off fat on soups or meat**
- **Use low-fat sauces like tomato or vegetable to serve with pasta and meat**

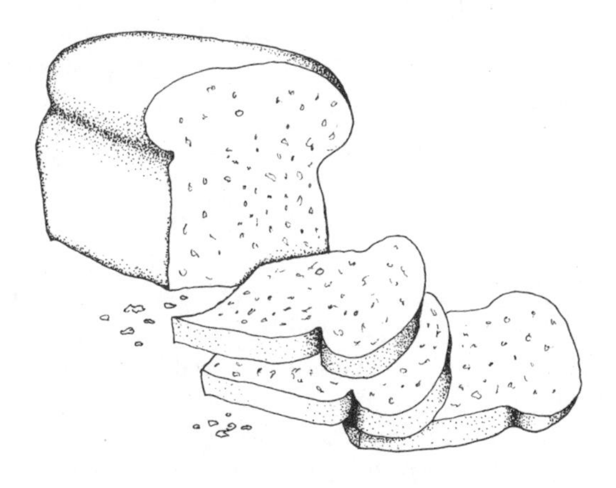

Healthy Cooking Techniques

The way you cook food is as important as what food you choose. In general, aim for the following when cooking:

- a minimal amount of additional fat
- retaining vitamin and nutrient content
- making food taste good
- using quick and easy cooking methods.

In practice, here are some useful tips.

Marinating

This is an excellent way to prepare food for healthy cooking. Marinating involves soaking food for some hours in different liquids and flavours. The marinade permeates the food, adding flavour whilst tenderising it and making it more moist when it comes to cooking.

A marinade usually contains an acid liquid like lemon juice, yoghurt, vinegar or wine, a little oil or maybe soya sauce and some herbs and spices. The longer the food is left to soak, the more intense the flavours. Timing is not critical, but should last for at least 30 minutes and can be up to two days.

Marinating is a wonderful way to prepare food for barbecuing, adding interesting flavours to meats, chicken and fish, and ensuring they do not dry out during cooking. Marinated foods can also be grilled, dry-fried, stir-fried or casseroled.

Grilling

Grilling food is an excellent alternative to frying. It does not require the addition of extra fat, and with meats like sausages and bacon it actually gets rid of some excess fat during the cooking process. Always use a grill grate that lets the fat drip into the pan below. Some foods may benefit from being basted with a minimum amount of oil during cooking, but you don't need much, so apply sparingly with a pastry brush.

Grilling is good for fish, especially oily kinds like mackerel, herring and sardines. Cook slowly and be careful not to overcook white fish, sprinkling it with water if it starts to dry out. Vegetables that grill well include tomatoes, mushrooms, peppers, aubergines and courgettes.

Frying

When we shallow- or deep-fry food we are adding extra fat to our diet. Limit the use of this cooking method and use the alternatives suggested. The results taste and look just as good. Chip-loving children will be happy with oven chips which contain less fat, and deep-fried foods can become a rare event.

Dry-frying

Try dry-frying. A non-stick pan is a good investment and gives the best results. Lightly smear the pan with oil, either using a pastry brush or kitchen paper. Heat the pan for a few seconds on high and then quickly lower it to a moderate heat. If you are using electricity, it may be necessary to lift the pan off the heat whilst the ring cools. Add the food and cook as required, reducing the heat to very low for the remainder of the cooking.

Stir-frying

This is a method of cooking that we associate with Chinese food. It is economical on fuel and requires the minimal addition of fat, but has many of the advantages of deep- and shallow-frying, including speed and preserving a good amount of nutrients and flavour. A wok is the best piece of equipment to use, but you can use a high-sided frying-pan, and even a large pot will do.

If using a wok it needs to be seasoned before first-time use, and from time to time if it goes rusty or loses its non-stick properties. This is done by heating a little oil inside, spreading it around and leaving it on a very low heat for 30 minutes. Wipe it out with kitchen paper to leave a blackened surface. After use, simply rinse immediately with warm water: do not use detergent. Oil the wok lightly before putting it away.

Stir-frying is a quick and easy way to cook if you follow these simple guidelines:

- prepare all ingredients before you start cooking, and add them in the order stated in the recipe as foods take different times to cook
- use evenly-sized ingredients: stir-frying cooks food very quickly, so cut pieces to the same size to ensure that all the ingredients cook in the same amount of time
- keep the food moving whilst cooking: stirring and turning the food is essential to make sure it cooks evenly. If food starts to stick, don't be tempted to add more oil. Simply add a tablespoon of water when this happens.

Most meats, fish and vegetables can be stir-fried, along with noodles and rice. Flavours and moisture can be added in the form of garlic, ginger and spices, with wine, soya sauce and stocks to make sauces. Meats and fish are often marinated beforehand to tenderise and add flavour.

Try experimenting with different meat and vegetable combinations. You don't have to use oriental ingredients, but whatever is in season. To make a simple sauce, just add some stock. If you want to be more adventurous, use soya sauce or try blackbean or oyster sauces, available from most supermarkets.

Steaming

The main advantage of steaming food is that it does not require any additional fat and is very good for vegetables as it retains far more nutrients, colour and flavouring than boiling. Fish and grains also steam well. It can also save on fuel if vegetables are steamed over boiling potatoes. You can buy purpose-built steamers, or improvise using a colander or metal sieve over a pan of boiling water. Cooking is quicker if you can put a lid on top. If not, use tin foil. Make sure the water does not touch the food and keep topping it up as it evaporates.

Reducing

We often use cream, sugar, salt, eggs and butter to taste and thicken sauces. However, we can get a far more healthy result by reducing liquids through evaporation to thicken and concentrate the flavour. This involves bringing the liquid to the boil and letting it bubble vigorously until the required thickness is achieved. Keep watching, as the liquid can dry up quickly. The wider the pan, the faster the reduction. Try thickening gravies this way.

Stewing and slow cooking

This can either be done on top of the cooker or in the oven, and involves the slow cooking of meats, fish and vegetables. It helps to develop good flavours and is an excellent way to cook cheaper cuts of meat to ensure they are not too tough. During the cooking process nutrients and vitamins are not lost as they transfer to the sauce.

Meat is best browned before casseroling as this seals it and adds colour and flavour to the sauce. Brown the meat in small batches, in a little oil over a high heat, and remove any excess fat before cooking the stew.

Casseroles are usually cooked with the lid on to make sure that the food does not dry out. If the sauce is too thin for your liking, leave the lid off for the last 20 minutes of cooking to let the liquid reduce. On the other hand, if it becomes too thick just add some stock, water or wine to get it to the consistency that you like.

If you are casseroling in the oven, it saves on fuel to bake potatoes at the same time.

Microwaving

The microwave is good for some types of food and pretty hopeless for others. It has the advantage of speed and convenience for reheating and defrosting, but in many cases is not as good as the conventional oven. However, it is good for retaining flavour and nutrients, and many people prefer fish which has been cooked in the microwave.

Food is either cooked dry or with a little water added to create steam. Vegetables work very well, with jacket potatoes taking under ten minutes. It is also very useful for reheating pre-prepared or left-over foods. Timing often needs a little practice, but try doing vegetables this way as it can also save on pots and pans. Always follow cooking instructions carefully.

Barbecuing

A barbecue has all the advantages of grill cooking – as well as being a lot of outdoor fun. Meats, fish and chicken can all be cooked this way. Try to steer clear of fatty hamburgers and sausages, and avoid shop-bought marinades that have a high fat and sugar content.

You can make your own hamburgers using lean mince, adding different herbs and spices for flavouring, but make sure that they are thoroughly cooked through. Fish can be cooked either whole on the bone or filleted and wrapped in tin foil, but be careful not to over-cook. Vegetables such as courgettes, mushrooms, peppers and aubergines are good cooked this way, either in pieces or on kebabs. Marinating food prior to cooking adds flavour and helps to tenderise meats.

About the Recipes

These imaginative recipes are healthy, tasty and simple. You'll find them easy to make, regardless of whether you are a beginner or a more experienced cook.

In general, the quantities given will feed at least four people. Where possible, the amount of the ingredient is expressed as a visual quantity rather than a specific weight – for instance, '1 medium onion'. Precise measurements are not normally necessary (except for baking or sauces) so you can add more of some ingredients, or make do with what you have. Use this approach when making up the light meals and snacks.

For some dishes you can reduce the meat content and 'bulk' out the meal with pulses or extra vegetables. This makes it a healthier option and it is also cheaper to prepare. If you find yourself feeding more mouths than you had planned for, simply add more ingredients that will bulk out the dish.

Cooking is not an exact science, and with practice and experience you will soon become a more confident cook.

The 28-Day Meal Plan

So, ready to make a start? Remember, all the menus that follow have been designed to correspond to Scotland's dietary target for the year 2005. But don't worry about the science of it all. We have translated the target theory into simple everyday eating. From now on, there really is an easy and appetising way to stick to a healthy diet.

The plan includes suggestions for light snack-type lunches, many of which do not even need a recipe. The main meal of the day consists of two courses, with three courses on Sundays.

Many of the dishes included are suitable for vegetarians, and vegetarian substitutions are often given as well. We also give you advice on what should be included in a healthy breakfast.

Finally, there are suggestions on how to structure other meals to make sure that you are eating healthily. Ideas to accompany the meals are given, but these are only suggestions, and specific recipes are not always included. The idea is to use good foods which are seasonal *and* offer best value.

Breakfast

Breakfast is an important meal so do not be tempted to skip it. Due to the long time the body goes without food, a person's energy requirements are greatest at this point.

Always start the day with a glass of fresh fruit juice, as this counts as one portion in the fruit and vegetable quota. Make sure that you are drinking a pure juice that has no added sugar or colourings.

Try to use wholegrain, high-fibre breakfast cereals or muesli, and avoid those with added sugar. Add semi-skimmed or skimmed milk and some fresh or dried fruit.

Eat brown, wholemeal or granary breads but go easy on the spreads. Use polyunsaturated margarines instead of butter, which is high in saturated fats. You can also cut the calories by using a low-fat alternative. Go for high-fruit/low-sugar jams or fruit-puree spreads, and try thinly spread yeast extract for a savoury option.

Breakfast should consist of:

- a glass of pure, unsweetened fruit juice
- a bowl of porridge or cereal/muesli (with no added sugar), eaten with skimmed or semi-skimmed milk or low-fat yoghurt, and fresh or dried fruit added
- two slices of toast, preferably wholemeal, with the recommended choice of spreads
- a cup of tea or coffee.

If you want a cooked breakfast at the weekend, remember to grill not fry, and poach or scramble your eggs in the microwave. Have baked beans to help lift your fibre content.

Light meals

It can be difficult to follow eating plans at times, so the light meal suggestions are foods that you can make up to take to work or can buy in the local shops or staff restaurant. Home-made soups are always a good option as they are filling and good vegetable and fibre providers.

Try to think of basing this meal on one of the following carbohydrate sources: bread, potato, rice or pasta – for example, a sandwich, a baked potato, or a rice or pasta salad.

Always include a piece of fresh fruit.

Main meals

The main meals in *Eat Yourself Healthy* are based on two courses, alternating starters and puddings. However, if you only wish to eat one course you can always finish your meal with a piece of fruit – a good time to add to your fruit intake if you have not managed to eat enough during the day.

Eat as much bread as you like with your main meal, but be sparing with the spread. Try eating bread with no butter or margarine, dipping it into your soup or using it to mop up sauces and gravies.

Try reducing the amount of meat that you eat with your main meal and increase the amount of vegetables, potatoes, pasta and rice. Introduce a salad with or at the end of your main meal.

The 28-Day Meal Plan

WEEK 1		
DAY	LIGHT MEAL	MAIN MEAL
Monday	Pitta pocket filled with apple, cucumber, tomato and lettuce Side salad Portion of fruit	Smoked mackerel pâté with cucumber and courgette salad and brown toast Cottage pie with carrots and broccoli
Tuesday	Large baked potato filled with cheese, tomato and lettuce Side salad ½ a melon	Pasta with tomato, vegetable and herb sauce Side salad and bread Rice pudding with peaches and cinnamon
Wednesday	Pasta salad with a brown roll Portion of fruit	Couscous with coriander, apricots and nuts Oat-stuffed mackerel served with boiled potatoes, green beans and sweetcorn
Thursday	Minestrone soup Ham, tomato and lettuce sandwich in granary bread Portion of fruit	Moroccan chicken with baked potatoes and salad Fresh bread Fresh fruit salad with low-fat yoghurt
Friday	Rice salad French bread with tomato Portion of fruit	Warm chicken-liver salad with crusty bread Salmon with red pepper and basil sauce, served with potatoes, spinach and turnip
Saturday	French-bread pizza with a salad Yoghurt with fresh fruit	Guacamole with vegetable sticks Chilli con carne and yoghurt and mint sauce, served with brown rice and a tomato and onion salad
Sunday	Sardines and toast Portion of fruit	Leek and potato soup with brown bread Roast pork with apple sauce, served with roast potatoes, and cabbage with grainy mustard, and peas Banana fool

WEEK 2		
DAY	**LIGHT MEAL**	**MAIN MEAL**
Monday	Hummus, with carrot and celery sticks and pitta bread Portion of fruit	Spicy lentil soup Chicken saag curry, with rice and nan bread served with raita and salad
Tuesday	Granary roll with ham, cucumber and tomato Portion of fruit	Fish and broccoli pie with salad Carrot cake
Wednesday	Rice salad with tuna and peppers French bread Portion of fruit	Cullen skink with warmed soda bread Liver with apple and onions served with mashed potatoes, green beans and cauliflower
Thursday	Baked potato with baked beans Portion of fruit	Pasta with bacon, mushroom and red pepper sauce Side salad and ciabatta bread Red wine jelly with pears
Friday	Carrot and oatmeal soup with wholemeal bread Pasta, apple, carrot and sultana salad Portion of fruit	Sardine pâté with lemon and a salad served with brown bread Beef and bean cassoulet with turnip and potatoes
Saturday	Ratatouille with thick chunks of granary bread Portion of fruit	Noodle soup with bread Stir-fry pork with broccoli served with rice
Sunday	Smoked mackerel salad with nutty bread Yoghurt and fruit	Scotch broth with bread Honey-roast chicken with oatmeal stuffing, served with roast potatoes, parsnips and cabbage Bramble and apple crumble

WEEK 3		
DAY	**LIGHT MEAL**	**MAIN MEAL**
Monday	Pitta pocket filled with tuna, onions, peppers and light mayonnaise Portion of fruit	Cock-a-leekie soup with bread Mince and tatties with skirlie, peas and cabbage
Tuesday	Tomato and orange soup Open chicken and apricot sandwich Portion of fruit	Baked fish with spring onion and ginger served with rice Side salad Caledonian ice-cream with raspberry coulis
Wednesday	Rice, ham and pineapple salad with bread Portion of fruit	Aubergine and thyme pâté with brown bread Lemon and garlic chicken, with baked potatoes, green beans and carrots Green salad
Thursday	Baked potato with cheese, coleslaw and salad Yoghurt Portion of fruit	Lasagne with salad and Italian bread Apple and ginger cake
Friday	Pasta salad with sweetcorn and peppers with a crusty roll Portion of fruit	Bean and vegetable soup with brown bread Herring in oatmeal with onion marmalade, served with salad
Saturday	Falafel with salsa, salad and pitta bread Portion of fruit	Gazpacho with bread Frittata with salad
Sunday	Baked sardines with brown bread and salad Portion of fruit	Yellow pea and bacon soup with blue cheese croutons Teriyaki roast lamb with new potatoes, carrots and broccoli Fruit brûlé

WEEK 4		
DAY	**LIGHT MEAL**	**MAIN MEAL**
Monday	Red pepper soup Baked potato filled with low-fat cheese, tomato and salad Portion of fruit	Brushetta Spinach and cheese cannelloni Side salad
Tuesday	Rice salad with kidney beans, peppers and sweetcorn Wholemeal roll Portion of fruit and yoghurt	Tuna with haricot beans and tomato, served with granary bread Tarragon chicken served with potatoes, cabbage and carrots
Wednesday	Courgette and mint soup Ham sandwich with tomato and coleslaw Portion of fruit	Salmon fishcakes with basil and tomato coulis, served with roasted vegetables and nutty bread Strawberry yoghurt ice-cream
Thursday	Baked potato with egg and tuna Portion of fruit	Parsnip, carrot and potato soup with bread Venison with mushrooms and red wine, served with potatoes, red cabbage and courgettes
Friday	Spinach and nutmeg soup with bread Bacon, lettuce and tomato bun Portion of fruit	Kedgeree with wholemeal bread Side salad Baked apples with fromage frais and pinenuts
Saturday	Spicy bean pâté with salad and bread Portion of fruit	Dahl Oriental pork with tomatoes, peppers and ginger, served with brown rice Side salad
Sunday	Mixed bean salad with bread Portion of fruit	Mushroom soup with bread Glazed ham, served with potatoes, broccoli and carrots Cranachan

The Recipes

Light Meals and Snacks

Healthy eating is made far easier with just a little planning. When we have very little in the cupboard, it's a good excuse to go for the convenience foods or pick up a take-away. These ideas should help to avoid this happening too often. They are quick and simple and use the type of ingredients that can become regulars in the shopping basket.

• *Baked potatoes* •

Cook for 1 hour at 190°C (375°F) or gas mark 5, and serve with the fillings below. Or cook in a microwave oven on full power for 10 minutes per potato. If you have to, use a low-fat spread instead of butter:

baked beans
low-fat cottage cheese with pineapple, chives or prawns
grated cheese with chopped tomato/ham/onion
low-fat coleslaw (grated cabbage and carrot, with a mixture of light mayonnaise and yoghurt)
grated carrot and apple
tuna with green pepper/tomato/onion
sweetcorn, celery and ham
smoked mackerel and cheese/onion/tomato
Mexican bean salad (kidney beans, sweetcorn and chopped pepper)

• *Pitta pockets* •

Use a salad base of lettuce, cucumber and tomato, and top with:

chicken and apple/orange and light mayonnaise or yoghurt
cheese and coleslaw
chilli (see p. 39)
chicken, pineapple, mayonnaise and curry powder

tuna and sweetcorn
sardines in tomato sauce (p. 31)
fromage frais and avocado

• *Pasta and rice salads* •

Cook the pasta or rice according to the instructions, rinse under cold water and mix with the following ingredients:

mandarin oranges, dill, yoghurt and light mayonnaise
peppers, onion, sweetcorn and kidney beans
courgettes, tomato, basil and onion
apples, oranges and sultanas
tuna, peppers and onion
ham and pineapple

BREADS

No shop-bought variety ever tastes as good as home-made bread. The wonderful smell of freshly baked bread can't be beaten. Some breads require a lot of work in kneading and resting and can therefore be time-consuming to make. These recipes are quick and simple and use dried yeast. If you want to use 'easy blend' yeast, follow the instructions on the packet and remember to use the total quantity of water given in the recipe when you add the liquid to the flour to form the dough.

• *Irish soda bread* •

This bread uses bicarbonate of soda instead of yeast as the raising agent and gives a lovely result that tastes wonderful when eaten warm, straight from the oven. It uses yoghurt instead of the traditional buttermilk as it contains less fat.

450 g (1 lb) wholemeal flour
225 g (8 oz) strong white flour
1½ tsp bicarbonate of soda
pinch of salt
450 g (1 lb) low-fat yoghurt mixed with 150 ml (5 fl oz) water
1 level tbsp baking powder

Pre-heat the oven to 220°C (425°F) or gas mark 7. Place all the dry ingredients in a bowl and mix them together. Slowly pour in the yoghurt and knead lightly to form a pliable, moist dough. If it feels too wet and sticky, sprinkle in a little more flour. Flatten the dough into a round shape about 15 cm (6 inches) in diameter and cut a cross in the centre. Bake in the oven for 40–50 minutes. To check the loaf is cooked, tap it on the bottom. It will make a hollow sound when it is ready. Wrap in a clean tea-towel to prevent the crust becoming too hard. Serve either warm or cold.

• *Easy wholemeal bread* •

If you wish to make this bread with a lighter texture, use half strong white flour.

450 g (1 lb) wholemeal flour
1 tsp salt
350 ml (12 fl oz) hand-hot water
1 tsp brown sugar
2 level tsp dried yeast

Activate the yeast by adding it, with the sugar, to 75 ml (3 fl oz) of the hand-hot water in a measuring jug. Stir it once and leave it to stand for 10–15 minutes until a good froth has formed. Warm the flour and the salt together in a mixing bowl in the oven or the microwave. This helps to keep the yeast activated during the rising. Make a well in the centre of the flour, stir the yeast and pour it in. Use a spoon to mix the dough and slowly add the rest of the water until you have a smooth dough that leaves the bowl clean. The amount of water is only approximate and you may require more or less. If you end up with a sticky dough because you have added too much water, just add a little more flour.

Transfer the dough to a 900 g (2 lb) tin or two 450 g (1 lb) tins, stretching and shaping it to size. Press it around the edges to leave a rounded hump in the middle. Sprinkle with flour, cover the tin with a damp dish-cloth, and leave the dough to rise for 40 minutes in a warm place or 1 hour at room temperature.

Cook the bread in a pre-heated oven, 210°C (400°F) or gas mark 6, for 35–45 minutes and for a further 10 minutes turned upside-down in the tin, until it sounds hollow when tapped. Cool the bread on a wire tray.

• *Nutty bread* •

This recipe couldn't be easier. It makes two loaves and you don't even need bread tins. You can vary the nuts that you use and also add seeds and dried fruits. Just stick to the weights in the recipe. Good suggestions include pumpkin and sunflower seeds, chopped hazelnuts and peanuts, and sultanas, raisins and apricots.

15 g (½ oz) dried yeast (1 level tbsp)
1 tsp sugar
275 ml (9 fl oz) hand-hot water
125 g (4 oz) 'granary' flour
375 g (12 oz) strong white flour
1 tsp salt
2 tsp walnut oil
25 g (1 oz) vegetable margarine
50 g (2 oz) walnut pieces
50 g (2 oz) pinenuts
egg yolk or milk to brush

Activate the yeast by adding it to about 100 ml (3½ fl oz) of the hand-hot water and the sugar. Stir and leave for 10–15 minutes, until a good froth forms. Warm the flour and salt in the oven or microwave, add 1 teaspoon of the walnut oil and the margarine, and rub it in to form bread crumbs. Pour in the yeast mixture and the rest of the tepid water and mix into a dough that comes away from the sides of the bowl. You can adjust the texture by adding more water or flour, if required. Put the dough back in the bowl after oiling it with the remaining walnut oil and leave it to rise in a warm place for about 1 hour or until it has doubled in size. On a lightly floured surface, knead the nuts into the dough then divide it in two and form into sausage shapes about 30 cm (12 in.) in length. Put them on an oiled baking-sheet, well apart, and brush with the egg or milk. Cover with a damp dish-cloth and leave in a warm place for a further 40 minutes. Bake in a pre-heated oven, 220°C (425°F) or gas mark 7, for 25 minutes or until golden brown. Cool on a wire rack.

Buying sandwiches

If you are buying ready-made sandwiches, go for the low-fat , low calorie choices or those marked 'no mayonnaise'. Whenever possible, buy wholemeal bread with a good bulky salad filling.

Week 1

MONDAY

• *Smoked mackerel pâté* •

Fish pâtés are easy to make and can be made with low-fat, healthy ingredients. Use them in sandwiches or to fill pitta bread or as a starter with warm bread or toast. They make a filling lunch when served with a bowl of hot soup. This recipe is for mackerel, but you can also use drained tinned tuna or smoked trout.

2 smoked mackerel, skinned and boned
375 g (12 oz) low-fat cottage cheese
1 tbsp lemon juice
1 tsp horseradish sauce or a dash of Tabasco
seasoning
lemon wedges

Place all the ingredients in the food processor and mix to a smooth consistency. If you do not have a food processor, mash the fish, and then mix the ingredients together with a fork. Season with salt and pepper. Either serve immediately in rounded spoonfuls or refrigerate in a bowl or terrine and turn out to serve. You can decorate the pâté with lemon wedges and a salad, and serve with warmed bread or toast.

• *Cottage pie* •

This is a family favourite which is great served with vegetables or baked beans. If you wish to make it go further, you can add beans to the mince after it has been cooked. Frozen peas also go well – children love mixing them together with the pie. Don't feel you have to stick rigidly to the meat and potato ratios as you can use more potato to ensure your daily carbohydrate intake is achieved. Remember when preparing mashed potato that you will need more potato per person than you would normally use, but don't be tempted to add lots of butter or cream. You don't need it. Use milk to get the required consistency.

375 g (12 oz) lean minced beef or lamb

1 onion, chopped

3 carrots, chopped

1 beef or chicken stock cube dissolved in 300 ml (½ pt) hot water

1 pinch of dried mixed herbs (optional)

1 tin of baked beans (optional)

1 kg (2¼ lb) potatoes, peeled and cut into chunks

150 ml (¼ pt) semi-skimmed milk

seasoning

Brown the mince over a gentle heat. There should be just enough fat to prevent it from sticking but, if not, add a small amount of cooking oil. If there is a lot of excess fat, drain this off. Add the onions and carrots, cook for 10 minutes over a low heat then add the herbs and stock. Leave to simmer for 20 minutes until the mince is thick and not too runny, but still has enough moisture to form a gravy. If using baked beans, add them now and heat through. Cover with the potatoes which have been boiled for 20 minutes, seasoned and mashed with enough milk to give a creamy consistency. Grill the pie until golden brown, and serve immediately or keep warm in a low oven.

TUESDAY

• *Pasta with tomato, vegetable and herb sauce* •

Pasta is a quick and easy meal, providing lots of carbohydrate with very little fat if combined with the right sauces. There are lots of different pastas available – some dried and others fresh – and many different shapes and sizes. Just follow the manufacturer's cooking instructions and add a sauce. Your own home-made sauces are far less expensive than shop-bought varieties and don't feel you have to stick rigidly to the vegetables suggested. Use your own combinations and favourites.

basic tomato sauce (see below)
250 g (8 oz) mushrooms, sliced
1 green pepper, cut into strips
1 courgette, sliced
Parmesan cheese (optional)
500 g (1 lb) pasta

Simply heat the tomato sauce, add the vegetables and cook for 10 minutes. Meanwhile, cook the pasta as directed, drain, return to the pan and add the tomato and vegetable sauce. Serve topped with grated Parmesan cheese (optional).

• *Basic tomato sauce* •

This basic recipe has many uses and is very inexpensive and easy to make. Use it as a sauce for pasta alone, or add a combination of cooked chicken, ham, bacon or tuna fish with vegetables such as mushrooms, peppers, courgettes or broccoli. Add the sauce and some vegetables to the cooked chicken, meat (browned in a pan) or beans to make a quick casserole.

Alternatively, liquidise with a handful of fresh basil or a glass of orange juice to make a wonderful soup. If you don't use all the sauce, you can refrigerate it for up to 5 days or freeze it.

1 tbsp olive or vegetable oil
1 large onion, chopped
2 cloves of garlic, crushed or well chopped
2 tins of chopped tomatoes (400 g/14 oz each)
½ tsp dried or 1 tbsp fresh herbs
2 tbsp tomato puree
seasoning

Heat the oil, a frying-pan is best, and add the onions. Fry for 5 minutes until soft and then add the garlic, but don't let it brown as this can give a slightly bitter taste to the sauce. Add the tinned tomatoes, the herbs and seasoning. Cook the sauce for 20 minutes, until the liquid has reduced, and then add the tomato puree. Use as a basic pasta sauce or as directed in the recipes.

• *Rice pudding with peaches and cinnamon* •

The secret of a good rice pudding is slow cooking so that the starchy grains of rice cook without too much evaporation of the milk. You can use any fresh or tinned fruit, but avoid heavy syrup, and opt for fruit, canned in fruit juice to cut down on sugar and empty calories.

600 ml (1 pt) semi-skimmed milk
40 g (1½ oz) pudding rice
25 g (1 oz) sugar
a few drops of vanilla essence
½ tsp cinnamon
a handful of sultanas
1 tin of peaches or fresh fruit (400 g/14 oz)

Pre-heat the oven to 150°C (300°F) or gas mark 2. In a saucepan, heat the milk to just below boiling-point, and add the sugar, vanilla and cinnamon. Then pour over the rice, which has been scattered over the bottom of a baking-dish, add the sultanas and mix together. Place the dish in the bottom of the oven and bake for 90 minutes or until the rice is tender, creamy and not too dry. Stir the pudding every 15 minutes during the first hour of cooking, stirring in the skin. This gives the delicious creamy consistency. Serve with peaches.

WEDNESDAY

• *Couscous with coriander, apricots and nuts* •

Couscous is a good source of carbohydrate and makes a change to rice as an accompaniment to many dishes. This salad makes a good starter or can be served as a main course by adding cooked chicken or lamb. Couscous is easy to prepare and just needs to be added to hot water to fluff it up. It can be served cold as a salad or warmed through in the microwave or the oven as a main course.

200 g (7 oz) couscous
150 ml (¼ pt) hot water
150 ml (¼ pt) orange juice
1 red onion, finely chopped
100 g (4 oz) ready-to-eat apricots, sliced
1 red or green pepper, chopped
2 tbsp pinenuts or peanuts, roasted
2 tbsp fresh coriander, chopped
seasoning

Pour the hot water over the couscous and leave it to stand, covered with a tea towel, for 10 minutes. Add the orange juice and fluff up the couscous with a fork. Mix in the rest of the ingredients and serve with fresh bread.

• *Oat-stuffed mackerel* •

Mackerel in a comparatively inexpensive fish that really can be dressed up with a little imagination. Its rich taste goes well with the sharpness of the orange in this recipe.

4 mackerel, gutted
2 oranges, zest grated, flesh chopped
4 tbsp porridge oats
1 onion, finely chopped
1 tbsp fresh parsley, chopped
1 tbsp raisins
1 apple, grated
1 tsp dried rosemary or 4 sprigs fresh rosemary
300 ml (10 fl oz) cider or orange juice
seasoning

Pre-heat the oven to 190°C (375°F) or gas mark 5. Mix together the orange zest, chopped orange flesh, oats, onion, parsley, raisins and apple, and season. Divide the mixture equally between the four fish and stuff loosely, adding the sprig of rosemary last. Place the fish in an oven-proof dish and pour the cider or orange juice over. Cover with a lid or some tin foil and bake for 40 minutes in the oven. Remove the fish and transfer to a warmed serving dish. Reduce the juices in the pan by boiling rapidly, uncovered, to concentrate the flavours. Pour the juices over the fish and serve.

THURSDAY

• *Minestrone soup* •

This soup is based on pasta, beans and vegetables, and can provide a balanced, nutritious meal on its own, if eaten with fresh bread. Try varying the type of pasta and beans that you use and add whatever vegetables you have available. This recipe will feed up to eight people, so if you have any left over you can freeze it for up to 3 months.

1 tbsp vegetable oil (preferably olive oil)
1 large onion, chopped
1 clove of garlic, chopped
2 carrots, thinly sliced
2 celery sticks, thinly sliced
2 large potatoes, diced
1.5 l (2½ pts) stock or water
1 tin of tomatoes (400 g/14 oz)
1 tbsp fresh or 1 tsp dried herbs
100 g (4 oz) wholewheat pasta
175 g (6 oz) cooked or tinned flageolet or other beans
2 courgettes, cut into matchsticks (optional)
3 tbsp chopped parsley
grated Parmesan cheese to serve (optional)
seasoning

Fry the onion and garlic in the oil over a moderate heat for 5 minutes. Add the carrots, celery, potatoes, tomatoes, herbs and stock, season and simmer for 30 minutes, stirring occasionally. Add the pasta, beans and courgettes and cook for a further 15 minutes. Taste, and adjust the seasoning. Stir in the parsley, and serve hot with the parmesan.

> Root ginger is now readily available in most supermarkets. It looks like a small, knotted potato and can vary in size. To use, peel it carefully and either chop or grate it finely. The powdered stuff is no substitute.

• *Moroccan chicken* •

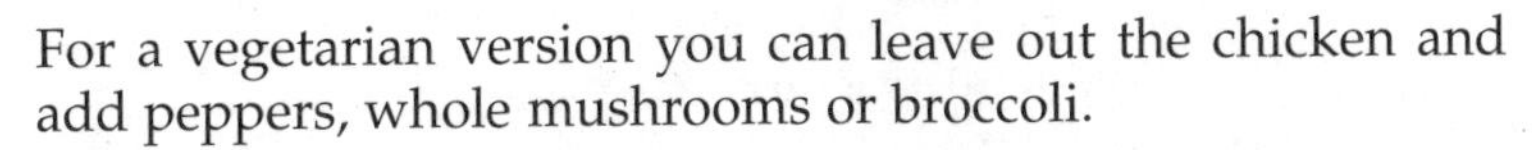

For a vegetarian version you can leave out the chicken and add peppers, whole mushrooms or broccoli.

4 chicken breasts or boneless thighs, cut into 6 pieces
½ tsp curry powder
½ tsp ground cinnamon
1 tsp ground cumin
1 tsp ground coriander
2 tsp root ginger, peeled and finely chopped
2 cloves of garlic, chopped
100 g (4 oz) dried apricots
150 ml (¼ pt) water
2 tsp vegetable oil
1 large onion, chopped
1 red pepper, sliced
1 tbsp tomato puree
1 tbsp vinegar
2 tsp sugar
1 tin of chickpeas (400 g/14 oz), drained

Mix the curry powder, cinnamon, cumin and coriander together, and rub half of it over the chicken, along with half of the garlic and ginger. Leave to marinate for 1 hour or longer. Simmer the apricots in the water for about 10 minutes or until tender. Heat the oil in a wok or large saucepan, add the onion and cook slowly for 5 minutes. Then add the chicken and remaining spices, garlic and ginger, and cook for a further 5 minutes. Add the red pepper, and stir in the tomato puree, vinegar, sugar, chickpeas and apricots and water. Simmer for 15 minutes and serve with baked potatoes and a side salad.

• *Fresh fruit salad* •

Choose fruits that are in season and therefore less expensive. If you have any left over, put it in the fridge and add it to your breakfast cereal.

2 oranges, peeled and cut into chunks
2 apples, cored and sliced
2 bananas, peeled and sliced
2 kiwi fruits, peeled and sliced
juice of 1 lemon
200 ml (⅓ pt) orange juice

Mix the apple and banana together with the lemon juice to prevent them from going brown. Add all the other ingredients and serve with fromage frais or yoghurt.

FRIDAY

• *Warm chicken-liver salad* •

This makes an impressive starter for a special dinner and a good main course for liver-lovers. Serve with hot crusty bread to mop up the juices. You can buy fresh chicken livers, usually from fishmongers, and frozen ones are available in most supermarkets. The livers are cooked very quickly over a high heat so that they are pink inside and crispy outside. The salad leaves can be bought pre-packed from supermarkets, or you can make up your own using different lettuce types and fresh spinach.

1 tbsp olive oil
250 g (8 oz) chicken livers, washed, trimmed and halved
250 ml (8 fl oz) fresh chicken stock or stock cube
3 cloves of garlic, crushed
3 tbsp wine, sherry or port (optional)
grated zest and juice of 1 lemon
1 tsp honey
1 tbsp fresh, chopped parsley
1 serving of mixed salad leaves per person
seasoning

Heat the oil in a large frying-pan, add the livers, and cook over a high heat for 2 minutes, shaking the pan frequently to turn the livers. Remove and drain them on kitchen paper, and then keep them warm in a low oven. Keep the heat under the frying-pan high, and add the stock and wine to the pan. Simmer until the volume has reduced by half, then add the lemon and honey and warm through. Season to taste, arrange the chicken livers on each plate on top of the salad leaves, and drizzle the sauce over, sprinkling with chopped parsley.

• *Salmon with red pepper and basil sauce* •

Salmon is no longer the expensive fish it used to be and is rich in beneficial fish oils. However, you can also use other fillets of fish in this recipe, such as cod, monkfish and mackerel. Grilled chicken breasts are also good. Try serving with pasta to soak up the lovely red sauce.

4 salmon fillets
vegetable oil
red pepper sauce (see below)
freshly-ground black pepper
fresh basil to serve

Season the salmon fillets with pepper and brush with a small amount of oil. Place them skin-side down under a medium heat and grill for 7–10 minutes or until cooked. (Baking the fish fillets in a medium oven for 15 minutes gives just as good results.) Be careful not to over-cook them as the fish will dry out. When cooked, the flesh should still be moist and slightly opaque. Spoon a pool of the red pepper sauce on to a plate and place the fish in the middle. Garnish with fresh basil.

• *Red pepper sauce* •

This sauce has a brilliant orange colour and goes well with chicken and fish. It can be served with pasta or boiled vegetables and makes a lovely soup with the addition of some liquid to thin out the consistency slightly. Although you can make the sauce without grilling the pepper, it is this process that gives the sauce its wonderful taste.

1–2 red peppers
1 medium onion, chopped
1 clove of garlic, crushed
½ tsp mixed or 1 tbsp fresh herbs, including basil and parsley
1 tin of tomatoes (400 g/14 oz)
seasoning

Cut the peppers into quarters, remove the seeds and flatten them out with the palm of your hand. Place, skin-side up, under a hot grill until they are black all over. Transfer the blackened peppers to a polythene bag, seal and leave for 10 minutes. Then remove them and peel off the skins. Cook the onion in the oil until it is just beginning to soften, add the garlic and fry for 1 minute. Now add the herbs, red peppers and tomato. Bring the sauce to the boil, season it and then simmer for 15 minutes. Liquidise the sauce until smooth.

SATURDAY

• *French bread pizza* •

This is a quick and easy way to make pizza, and children love making their own. The toppings here are only suggestions, so use your own favourites. Serve it as a snack lunch or with salads for a main meal. If you don't have time to make the tomato base, you can use shop-bought pizza topping.

1 stick of French bread
⅓ quantity of basic tomato sauce (see p. 31)
75 g (3 oz) mushrooms, sliced
110 g (4 oz) ham, chopped
1 onion, sliced
1 red or green pepper, diced
110 g (4 oz) grated Edam, cheddar or mozzarella cheese

Cut the loaf in half and split each half down the middle to give four bases. Cook the tomato sauce over a moderate heat until it has thickened to about 4 tablespoons in volume. Spread the sauce equally over each piece of bread and cover with the fillings, ending with the cheese on top. Either grill them under a slow heat until the cheese seems to bubble or cook in a pre-heated oven 180°C (350°F) or gas mark 4 for 12 minutes.

• *Guacamole with vegetable sticks* •

Guacamole is basically an avocado dip. It can be blended with a food processor, mashed with a fork or roughly diced. Avocados are ripe when they give only slightly when grasped in the hand like a ball. Too soft and the flesh may be brown. If the avocado is very firm, it is best diced like a salsa. If it is mushy, mash or process it. Remember you can vary the ingredients to suit your tastes. Yoghurt has been added to this recipe as it makes it go further, but if you want a more intense avocado flavour, leave it out. You can also try adding red onion, fresh coriander and chopped tomato, as they are especially good if the mixture is finely diced.

2 ripe avocados
juice of 1 lemon or lime
dash of Tabasco or 1 fresh chopped green chilli or a pinch of chilli powder
½ small onion, finely chopped
1 clove of garlic, crushed
1 small carton of low-fat yoghurt or fromage frais
2 carrots, 1 pepper, 6 sticks of celery and ½ cucumber, all cut into pencil-thick sticks
pitta bread pieces

Quarter the avocados, remove the stones and peel away the skin. Either process, mash or dice the flesh, adding the lemon juice, onion, garlic and yoghurt (optional). Serve with the vegetable sticks and hot pitta bread.

• *Chilli con carne* •

This dish is based on meat, but a vegetarian alternative can easily be made by increasing the quantities of vegetables and beans and leaving out the meat. You can also adapt the recipe to your own requirements by adjusting the meat to vegetable-and-bean ratio. Chilli is good served with brown rice, which has a lovely nutty flavour and is further complimented by a yoghurt and mint sauce. Instead of rice, try some warmed brown pitta bread.

240 g (8 oz) lean minced beef
1 onion, chopped
2 carrots, chopped
1 clove of garlic, crushed
1 tin of tomatoes (400 g/14 oz), chopped
½ tsp chilli powder/cayenne pepper (or to taste)
2 tbsp tomato puree
1 tin of red kidney beans (400 g/14 oz) , drained (or any other cooked beans)
1 tin of sweetcorn (400 g/14 oz)
1 green pepper, chopped
225 g (8 oz) brown rice (cooked according to the packet)
or
4 pieces of brown pitta bread, warmed under the grill
1 small carton of yoghurt
1 tbsp fresh mint, chopped, or ½ tsp dried mint

In a large heavy-based pan, brown the mince over a low heat. There is no need to add extra oil, just stir from time to time to stop the mince from sticking. Pour off any excess fat, add the onion, garlic and carrot and cook for 5 minutes, giving it the occasional stir to mix the ingredients. Add the tomatoes, chilli powder and tomato puree, stir, then leave to cook over a low heat for 30 minutes. By this time the liquid from the tomatoes will have reduced, and the consistency should not be too runny. If it is, leave to cook for 15 minutes more. Add the beans, sweetcorn and pepper and cook for a further 15 minutes. Serve with bread or rice, accompanied by the mint yoghurt

Vegetarian options

Many recipes, especially stews and casseroles, can use beans and pulses as an alternative to meat. Good options include chickpeas, haricot beans, black beans, kidney beans, lentils, flageolet beans and broad beans. Either cook them as instructed, or use the tinned varieties that are already pre-cooked. Simply omit the meat from the recipe and add the pre-cooked beans near the end of cooking to warm them through.

SUNDAY

• *Leek and potato soup* •

This soup is very filling but not high in calories. It tastes very creamy but has no cream added to it – the potato is responsible for giving it the lovely texture. You don't have to be too precise about quantities, so add whatever amounts you have. A little more potato and a little less leek will do no harm. You can even leave out the leek altogether and turn this into celery soup. If you don't have a food processor or liquidiser, leave the soup whole as it tastes just as good.

1 tbsp vegetable oil
1 onion, chopped
3 leeks, washed and sliced, using the green bits if they are clean
2 sticks of celery, chopped
2 medium potatoes, chopped
1 tsp curry powder (optional)
500 ml (1 pt) chicken stock or water
seasoning

Heat the oil in a large saucepan, add the onions and soften for 5 minutes. Then add the rest of the vegetables and curry powder and cook for another 5 minutes, stirring frequently. Add the liquid – you might need to add some more water to ensure that the vegetables are all covered – bring to the boil and simmer gently for 30 minutes. Puree with a blender, season to taste, reheat and serve.

• *Roast pork with apple sauce and roast potatoes* •

Pork is a rich meat. It needs a minimum of flavours added, and goes very well with fruit sauces. All cuts of pork are tender and suitable for roasting, but try to avoid joints that have a lot of fat, like the belly. When serving, avoid the fatty parts. Cook pork in a pre-heated oven at 180°C (350°F) or gas mark 4 for 35 minutes per 500 g (1 lb) plus 35 minutes. Make gravy from the roasting juices, but remember to drain off the fat. Putting the flour, vegetables and herbs under the pork whilst roasting creates a lovely gravy. Pork is good with cabbage, which has been cooked and then mixed with a tablespoon of grainy mustard.

1 kg (2 lb) joint of pork
1 carrot, sliced
1 onion, sliced
1 tbsp flour
1 tsp dried or 1 tbsp fresh herbs
seasoning
50 ml (2 fl oz) cider or apple juice (optional)
1 stock cube, dissolved in 100 ml (4 fl oz) hot water
500 g (1 lb) potatoes, peeled and cut if big
1 tbsp vegetable oil
2 large cooking apples, peeled, cored and chopped
1 tsp sugar (optional)

Place the flour, carrots, onion and herbs in a the bottom of a metal roasting-dish, put the pork on top and season. Roast in the pre-heated oven as per weight. Meanwhile, make the apple sauce by placing the apples in a saucepan over a low heat and cooking gently for 10 minutes until a puree has formed. Taste and add sugar and a little water if required. Serve either hot or cold.

About 40 minutes before the pork has finished cooking, heat the vegetable oil on a metal tray in the oven and add the potatoes, turning them over to cover them in the oil. Put the potatoes in the oven. At this time add the stock to the roasting-pan. When the pork is removed, leave it to rest for 20 minutes before carving, and increase the oven temperature to 220°C (425°F) or gas mark 7 to finish cooking the potatoes.

Meanwhile, make the gravy. Stir the contents of the roasting-tin to mix in the flour, then add the cider or apple juice (optional). Cook over a medium heat for 3 minutes, then sieve it to give a smooth gravy. Remove the potatoes from the oven when they are golden brown, carve the pork and serve along with the gravy and apple sauce.

• *Banana fool* •

Fools are normally made with whipped cream. Here fromage frais is used which has a lower fat content than cream, giving it a lighter taste and texture. The natural sweetness of the bananas means that minimal sweetener is required. In fact, you can leave it out if you wish. You can also try substituting other pureed fruits for the banana, and fresh or drained tinned peaches make a good alternative. The dessert is best eaten on the day of making.

4 bananas
1 carton low-fat fromage frais (250 g)
1 tbsp icing sugar

Liquidise or mash the banana and icing sugar together. Fold in the fromage frais, and spoon into individual glasses. Chill until required.

Week 2

MONDAY

• *Hummus* •

This makes a lovely dip to serve with vegetable sticks and pitta bread, and also makes a good sandwich filling. You can use tinned chickpeas, but remember to take the weight without the water. Tahini is a paste made from sesame seeds, and is available in larger supermarkets and health food shops.

250 g (8 oz) dried chickpeas, soaked then cooked, or 1 tin cooked chickpeas (400 g/14 oz)
juice of 2 lemons
2 tbsp tahini
2 cloves of garlic, crushed
pinch of ground cumin

Soak the chickpeas in plenty of water for several hours or overnight. Drain and rinse them thoroughly. Place them in a pan with fresh cold water, bring them to the boil, and boil rapidly for 10 minutes. This is important to get rid of poisonous toxins. Reduce the heat, cover and simmer for 1 hour or until tender. In a food processor, process the chickpeas to a smooth paste. Then puree all the ingredients together to form a smooth paste, season and add water, if required.

• *Spicy lentil soup* •

Spices are added to this soup to give an Eastern flavour, but you can leave them out if you wish. Orange split lentils need no soaking so it is a quick soup to make. If you wish to use green or brown lentils, remember to soak them first. You can add whatever vegetables you happen to have, such as parsnips, carrots, leeks and cabbage, so experiment and see what you come up with. The quantities in this recipe will serve 8, or 6 large servings.

1 onion, chopped
3 carrots, chopped
4 celery stalks, chopped
1 tin of tomatoes (400 g/14 oz)
450 g (1 lb) orange split lentils
2 cloves of garlic, crushed
1 tbsp ground cumin
1 tsp ground coriander
2 l (4 pts) water or stock

Place all the ingredients in a large soup pot and bring to the boil. Leave to simmer gently for 30 minutes, then serve.

• *Chicken saag curry* •

You can make this curry as mild or as strong as you wish by altering the amount of chilli (or cayenne) pepper that you add. As well as, or instead of, the spinach, you can add lentils to make a type of dhal. By leaving out the chicken and adding lentils, you have a wonderful vegetarian option. Serve with raita – a mixture of natural yoghurt and chopped cucumber or mint.

1 tbsp vegetable oil
1 large onion, chopped
4 cloves of garlic, crushed
1 tbsp freshly grated ginger
1 heaped tsp ground cumin
1 heaped tsp ground coriander
½ tsp chilli powder
2–3 chicken breasts, cut into chunks, or 8 thigh and leg joints
2 tins of tomatoes (400 g/14 oz each)
1 packet of frozen spinach (450 g/1 lb)

Heat the oil in a large saucepan over a medium heat, add the onions and soften for 5 minutes. Next, add the garlic and cook for another 2 minutes, making sure that it does not burn. Stir in the ginger, cumin, coriander and chilli, and then add the chicken and cook for 5 minutes over a low heat. Add the tomatoes to cover the chicken, and cook for a further 30 minutes if using breast or 45 minutes if using chicken joints. Defrost, drain and chop the spinach and stir through 5 minutes before serving. Serve with rice and nan bread.

TUESDAY

• *Fish and broccoli pie* •

Fish pie can look very anaemic, so this one includes tomatoes and broccoli to liven up the colour. You can also use mushrooms to add flavour. Using smoked fish adds a lovely taste, and use whatever unsmoked fish is available – cod, plaice, haddock and mackerel are all good. Fish pies are simple to make and involve binding together the fish and vegetables with a sauce and topping with mashed potatoes. Another variation is to add cabbage to the potato topping. Do try adding the nutmeg – only a sprinkling – to the potatoes, as it gives them a wonderful taste. You can also add hard-boiled eggs to the fish mixture for a change, or increase the proportion of smoked fish in the recipe, if you like.

250 g (8 oz) smoked fish
450 g (1 lb) unsmoked fish
1 onion, finely chopped
1 bay leaf
500 ml (1 pt) semi-skimmed milk
50 g (2 oz) mature cheddar, grated
2 tsp dried or 2 tbsp fresh parsley
2 tomatoes, quartered
250 g (8 oz) broccoli spears
3 hard-boiled eggs (optional)
white sauce (see below)
1 kg (2 lb) freshly cooked potatoes
150 ml (¼ pt) semi-skimmed milk
a little freshly grated nutmeg (optional)

Pre-heat the oven to 210°C (400°F) or gas mark 6. Place the fish in a pan, add the onion and bay leaf, and cover with the milk (500 ml/1 pint) that will be used in the white sauce recipe. Bring it gently to the boil and simmer for 2 minutes. Turn off the heat and set it aside for 20 minutes or so. Drain the milk from the fish and use it to make the white sauce. Flake the fish lightly with a fork and add it, along with the cheese, tomatoes, parsley, broccoli and eggs (optional) to the white sauce and gently mix together. Now pour the mixture into a baking-dish. Mash the potatoes with the nutmeg and milk – although don't add it all at once, just add enough to give a firm mixture – and spread it evenly over the fish mixture using the back of a spoon. Bake in the pre-heated oven 20 minutes or until heated through and browned.

• *White sauce* •

A basic béchamel or white sauce is a milk sauce that is thickened using a mixture of flour and fat known as a roux. It has many uses and often has other ingredients added to it such as cheese, parsley, onions and mustard. It is used in macaroni cheese, cauliflower cheese, lasagne and fish pie. Always cook the sauce for 5–10 minutes after it has thickened to get rid of the 'raw' flavour of the flour. Also, the liquid used must be cold to start off with.

For ½ litre/1 pt (approx.):

25 g (1 oz) vegetable margarine

25 g (1 oz) flour (white or brown)

425 ml (¾ pt) cold milk (or half-milk, half-stock)

seasoning

This quick and easy version is made by placing all the ingredients in a saucepan over a medium heat and whisking with a balloon whisk until bubbles start to form and the sauce thickens. Turn the heat down low and leave to cook for 5 minutes, stirring occasionally. You must whisk the sauce continuously or it may go lumpy. Season to taste.

• *Carrot cake* •

This cake makes a healthy option to shop-bought cakes and biscuits. It uses wholemeal flour, which is high in fibre, has minimal sugar and uses polyunsaturated oil instead of butter. It is very moist and has a high fruit and vegetable content. Children love it, so try it in their lunch boxes. You can also try adding walnuts and sunflower seeds for a change. If you are using plain instead of self-raising wholemeal flour, add an extra 2 tsp of baking powder.

2 medium carrots, grated (approx. 175 g/6 oz)

2 eggs

100 g (4 oz) sugar

100 g (4 oz) self-raising wholemeal flour

1 tsp baking powder

75 ml (3 fl oz) vegetable oil

1 tsp ground cinnamon

½ tsp ground nutmeg

50 g (2 oz) desiccated coconut (optional)

50 g (2 oz) raisins (optional)

Pre-heat the oven to 190°C (375°F) or gas mark 5. Grease and line the base of a 18 cm/7 in. square tin. Whisk the eggs and sugar together and slowly whisk in the oil. Add the remaining ingredients, sieving the flour, and mix together. Pour the mixture into the tin and bake in the pre-heated oven for 20–25 minutes, until firm to touch. Turn out and cool on a wire tray.

WEDNESDAY

• *Cullen skink (smoked haddock soup)* •

This is a traditional Scottish soup. It can either be left chunky, or liquidised to give a smoother texture. Traditionally, this recipe used whole Finnan haddock, but you can use any kind of smoked white fish. Arbroath Smokies are very good. Try to get undyed fish.

450 g (1 lb) smoked haddock fillets
300 ml (½ pt) water
2 onions, chopped
4 large potatoes, cut into chunks
450 ml (¾ pt) semi-skimmed milk
seasoning
fresh parsley, chopped

Boil the haddock in the water for 5 minutes, remove, flake with a fork and put aside. Add the onions and potatoes to the cooking water, season with pepper and simmer for 15 minutes. Remove the pan from the heat and use a fork to mash the potatoes roughly. Add the milk and bring it to the boil. Return the fish, season to taste and heat through. You can either serve the soup like this or liquidise it for a smoother texture. Serve hot with the parsley.

• *Liver with apple and onions* •

Liver is an inexpensive meat that can be made to go a long way. Adding the apples and onions gives a sweet flavour and increases the fibre content. This dish is good served with potatoes mashed with skimmed milk and steamed cabbage.

450 g (1 lb) lambs' liver, washed
3 medium onions, sliced
2 dessert apples, cored and sliced (skin on)
2 tbsp vegetable oil
150 ml (¼ pt) white wine or chicken stock
large pinch of dried sage
seasoning

Fry the onions until golden brown in the oil over a low heat for 20 minutes. After 15 minutes add the apple. If they start to stick, add a little water. Turn up the heat to medium, add the liver and sage, and stir-fry for 3 minutes, letting the liver colour. Add the wine or stock, stir well and let it reduce for a few minutes until a sauce consistency is achieved. Season with pepper and serve as above or with a mixed salad and crusty bread.

THURSDAY

• *Pasta with bacon, mushroom and red pepper sauce* •

Use whatever pasta you like for this recipe – spaghetti is good, and so are pasta bows and penne. Both fresh and dried pasta are suitable, so just follow the instructions on the packet. If you wish to make a vegetarian option, leave out the bacon and add other vegetables that you have available.

450 g (1 lb) pasta
2 quantities of red pepper sauce (see p. 37)
1 tbsp olive or vegetable oil
4 rashers of bacon, chopped
225 g (8 oz) mushrooms, sliced
a handful of fresh basil leaves, chopped
seasoning

Fry the bacon and the mushrooms in the oil for 5 minutes, add the red pepper sauce and simmer for another 5 minutes. Meanwhile, cook the pasta as instructed on the packet. When cooked, drain and add the pepper, bacon and mushroom sauce and serve.

• *Red wine jelly* •

This pudding has no added sugar but, if you find it lacks sweetness, you can substitute concentrated apple juice for some of the wine. It is lovely served on its own or with fresh fruit, and can be moulded in one large dish or in individual wine glasses.

300 ml (½ pt) red wine
1 stick of cinnamon
rind of 1 orange
4 cloves
8 tbsp orange juice
15 g (½ oz) or 1 envelope gelatine

Place the wine, cinnamon stick, orange rind and cloves in a saucepan. Heat to just below boiling-point, remove and leave to infuse for 30 minutes. Measure the orange juice into a pan, scatter the gelatine powder into it and leave it to become spongy. Then heat gently until it melts. Strain the infused wine and add the gelatine and orange mixture, stirring well. Then pour the mixture into a wet 600 ml (1 pt) jelly mould or four individual glasses. Refrigerate for 2–3 hours or until the jelly has set. To serve, dip the mould into warm water to loosen the jelly and invert it on to a plate. Alternatively, serve in the wine glasses.

FRIDAY

• *Carrot and oatmeal soup* •

Oatmeal is used in many traditional Scottish recipes to thicken soups and stews, giving them a creamy body. As in other recipes, the quantities used do not need to be exact – there or there about will do.

1 tbsp vegetable oil
2 leeks, thinly sliced
450 g (1 lb) carrots, thinly sliced
1 l (2 pts) stock or water
juice and zest of 1 orange
25 g (1 oz) fine or medium oatmeal
3 tbsp milk
seasoning
fresh parsley to garnish

Sweat the leeks in the oil over a low heat for 5 minutes then add the carrots and cook for a further 5 minutes. Add the stock, orange zest and seasoning and simmer for 30 minutes.

Meanwhile, soak the oatmeal in the milk for 15 minutes and add to the soup to cook for the last 15 minutes. Add the orange juice and simmer for 5 minutes more, then liquidise and serve hot, garnished with parsley.

• *Sardine pate* •

This makes a quick and easy starter. You can use boned fresh sardines with a dash of tomato puree, but tinned are just as good.

1 tin of sardines in tomato sauce (120 g/4 oz)
200 g (7 oz) low-fat soft white cheese
50 g (2 oz) fresh wholemeal bread crumbs
a dash of Tabasco (optional)

Place all the ingredients in a food processor and blend to a smooth pâté. Transfer to the fridge in a small bowl and cool for at least 1 hour before serving with hot toast or oatcakes.

• *Cassoulet* •

Cassoulet is a traditional French dish. It consists of meat, beans and vegetables, cooked together with herbs. The cassoulet gives great scope for variation. You can use either beef, lamb or pork, or a mixture of meats. Use haricot, flageolet or butter beans and add some lentils if you wish. It is a very filling meal and is good served with crusty bread and a salad. As the dish is cooked for a long time to develop the flavours, less expensive cuts of meat can be used – but do cut off any bits of excess fat.

275 g (10 oz) haricot or flageolet beans, soaked overnight and boiled rapidly for 10 minutes, or tinned beans
500 ml (1 pt) stock or water
1 onion, chopped
1 leek, chopped
2 celery stalks, chopped
2 carrots, sliced
2 cloves of garlic, crushed
450 g (1 lb) meat
1 glass red wine (optional)
1 tin of tomatoes (400 g/14 oz)
2 tbsp tomato puree
2 courgettes, sliced
175 g (6 oz) green beans
seasoning

In a lidded casserole dish, place the beans with the onion, leek, carrot, celery and garlic in the stock and cook for 1 hour in the oven at 150°C (300°F) or gas mark 2. Then add the rest of the ingredients, apart from the courgettes and green beans, and cook for a further 3 hours, or until the meat is tender and the beans are cooked. Add the courgettes and greens beans for the last 15 minutes of cooking. Season and serve.

SATURDAY

• *Ratatouille* •

This is an other French dish. The authentic version is rather heavy on the oil so the method used in this recipe cuts down on this ingredient. Ratatouille makes a meal in itself, served with salad and bread. It is also good served as a vegetable dish with grilled chicken and lamb. It also makes the basis of a good vegetarian lasagne when substituted for the meat and tomato sauce of the traditional recipe.

1 aubergine
1 tbsp vegetable oil, preferably olive oil
1 large onion, sliced
3 cloves of garlic, crushed
1 red pepper, chopped
1 green pepper, chopped
1 yellow pepper, chopped
2 tins of tomatoes (400 g/14 oz each)
1 tsp dried herbs or 1 tbsp fresh herbs
seasoning

Pre-heat the oven to 170°C (325°F) or gas mark 3. Slice the aubergine into thick rounds, sprinkle with salt on both sides and leave to sweat on absorbent kitchen paper for 30 minutes. This takes out any bitter juices from the aubergine. Rinse in cold water, brush the aubergine slices with oil and then place them under a hot grill and cook for 5 minutes, turning once. The aubergine will start to soften, but don't let it burn. Meanwhile, soften the onion and garlic in some oil over a low heat in a casserole. Once the aubergine is cooked, add it to the casserole along with all the other ingredients. Cook in the oven for 40 minutes with the lid on. This dish can also be cooked on the cooker top in a large saucepan over a low heat. Stir occasionally to incorporate the tomatoes, and if the liquid is too runny, take the lid off for the last 15 minutes to allow some of the liquid to evaporate. Season to taste and serve.

• *Chicken noodle soup* •

This is a quick soup that can be made using store cupboard ingredients. If you don't have chicken then chicken stock on its own will do and you can add other ingredients such as cabbage, sweetcorn and beansprouts to ring the changes.

150 g (5 oz) Chinese egg noodles or broken spaghetti
1 l (2 pts) of chicken stock
100 g (4 oz) cooked chicken
4 spring onions, chopped
1 tsp sesame oil (optional)
soya sauce to season

Cook the noodles or spaghetti in the stock as per the instructions. One minute before the end of cooking time add the spring onions, chicken and sesame oil. Return to the boil and serve with soya sauce to season, and bread.

• *Stir-fry pork with vegetables* •

This recipe can be used for any kind of meat or fish, and you can also vary the types and quantities of vegetables you use, depending on what you have available. To make a vegetarian option, just leave out the meat. A wok is best for this form of cooking, but a large frying-pan will do. Serve as a meal in itself or with boiled brown rice or noodles.

2 tsp vegetable oil
1 large onion, chopped
2 carrots, peeled and cut into match sticks
1 clove of garlic, crushed
2.5 cm (1 in.) fresh root ginger, peeled and finely chopped
275 g (10 oz) pork fillet, cut into thin strips
¼ white or green cabbage, finely chopped
250 g (8 oz) broccoli, divided into small spears
1 red or green pepper, sliced lenthwise (optional)
250 g (8 oz) beansprouts
1 tbsp dry sherry
2 tbsp soya sauce

Heat the wok and add the oil when hot. Stir-fry the onions and carrots for 3 minutes, then add the ginger and garlic and cook for a further 2 minutes. If the ingredients start to stick at any time, do not be tempted to add more oil. Add 1 tbsp of water and that should do the trick. Remove the vegetables from the wok, add the pork and cook for 3 minutes, then return the onion and carrot mixture along with the cabbage, broccoli, pepper and beansprouts and stir-fry for a further 2 minutes. Add the sherry and soya sauce, turn down the heat, warm through and serve.

SUNDAY

• *Scotch broth* •

There is no definitive recipe for Scotch broth. It is basically a vegetable and barley soup, so don't feel that you have to stick rigidly to the ingredients. The quantities are guidelines only and can be varied to suit personal taste and availability of ingredients. This soup makes a meal on its own, so try adding more potatoes to the pot and serving with chunky, warm brown bread.

225 g (8 oz) barley or broth mix
2 carrots, diced
1 onion, chopped
1 turnip, diced
3 celery stocks, sliced
2 potatoes, diced
1.5 l (3 pts) stock or water
1 tbsp fresh or 1 tsp dried parsley
seasoning

Put the stock and barley in a large saucepan and simmer for 30 minutes. Skim off any scum that forms on the surface. Add the vegetables, season and cover, simmering for a further hour and stirring occasionally. Add the parsley 5 minutes before serving.

• *Honey roast chicken with oatmeal stuffing* •

The chicken is coated in honey and salt, to seal in the flavours and moisture and add to the taste of the gravy. Vegetables and a little flour are placed under the bird during cooking to add to the taste of the juices and help to thicken the gravy slightly.

Liquid is also added to the roasting-dish to keep the bird moist and stop the honey burning. Served with baked potatoes cooked in the oven at the same time as the chicken, this meal is a real feast.

1 medium chicken
2 tbsp runny honey
1 tbsp rock salt
½ onion, sliced
½ carrot, sliced
2 tsp dried or 2 tbsp fresh herbs
1 glass white wine (optional)
300 ml (½ pt) chicken stock

For the stuffing:

1 medium onion, finely chopped
1 tsp dried herbs or 1 tbsp fresh herbs
1 tbsp flour
100 g (4 oz) medium oatmeal
25 g (1 oz) vegetable margarine
2 tbsp water

Pre-heat the oven to 180°C (350°F) or gas mark 4. To make the stuffing, simply mix all the ingredients together, and spoon them into the body cavity. During cooking, the oatmeal will swell and absorb the chicken juices and cook to a delicious nutty flavour. Then put the onion, carrot, herbs and flour in a roasting-dish and place the stuffed chicken on top. Drizzle the honey over the chicken and sprinkle the salt on top. Place in the pre-heated oven and cook for either 35 minutes per 500 g plus 25 minutes, or 20 minutes per pound plus 20 minutes, remembering to add the weight of the stuffing to this calculation.

After 20 minutes, add the stock to the bottom of the roasting-dish and keep checking that it does not dry out. Add more water if it does. Remove the chicken from the oven when cooked and leave it to rest on a warm plate, covered in tin foil, for 20 minutes before carving. Meanwhile, make the gravy by stirring together the contents of the roasting dish, returning this to a low heat on the cooker top and adding the wine. You may have to add a little more water to thin the gravy down. Simmer for 5 minutes or until the correct thickness is reached. Then strain, remove the fat and serve with the carved chicken and stuffing.

• *Bramble and apple crumble* •

This is a very easy and versatile pudding to make. Once you have mastered the art of making the crumble topping, the different fillings are endless. Suggestions include: dried apricot and apple, cinnamon and pear, peach and apple, raspberry and strawberry, and blackcurrant and apple. You can use fresh fruits in season or tinned fruits in natural, unsweetened juices. Use concentrated apple juice, available from health food shops, to sweeten the fruit mixtures instead of sugar.

Brambles grow wild and you should be able to pick your own in September. If not, use tinned blackberries (as they are known south of the Border) or an alternative fruit.

2 large cooking apples, peeled, cored and thinly sliced

450 g (1 lb) brambles

6 tbsp apple juice concentrate or 1 tbsp sugar and 5 tbsp water

For the topping:

150 g (5 oz) wholewheat flour

1 tbsp oatmeal

75 g (3 oz) vegetable margarine

3 tbsp toasted sesame seeds or sunflower seeds

1–2 tbsp brown sugar

1 tsp cinnamon

Pre-heat the oven to 170°C (325°F) or gas mark 3. Simmer the apples and brambles together with either the apple juice concentrate or the sugar and water solution for 3 minutes. Turn the mixture into a shallow baking-dish. Rub together the flour and margarine until they resemble crumbs, then add the oatmeal, sesame or sunflower seeds, sugar and cinnamon. Sprinkle the topping over the fruit and bake in the oven for 40 minutes or until it is brown on top. Serve warm with low-fat yoghurt or fromage frais.

Week 3

MONDAY

• *Cock-a-leekie soup* •

This is a traditional Scottish soup made with leeks and chicken. This recipe has rice added to it to make it more substantial and feed more mouths, but for a more authentic version you can leave this out. Traditionally a whole chicken is boiled and this will feed up to ten people. You can also use the left-over carcass and meat from a roast chicken, if available.

2 chicken joints
2 leeks, chopped
1 l (2 pts) chicken stock or water
1 bay leaf
½ tsp dried or 1 tbsp fresh thyme
½ tsp dried or 1 tbsp fresh parsley
50 g (2 oz) rice
12 pitted prunes
seasoning

Place the chicken, leeks, stock or water, rice and herbs in a large saucepan, bring them to the boil and simmer for 40 minutes. Take out the chicken and remove the meat from the bones with a fork, tearing it into shreds. Return the meat to the pan along with the prunes and the pepper, stir and heat through.

• *Mince and tatties with skirlie* •

Mince, if cooked well, makes a lovely warming meal. For this dish there are many different things you can add to the potatoes to make them more interesting: mashed turnips and chives to make 'clapshot'; cooked cabbage to make 'rumbledethumbs'; and either spring onions or mashed carrots and turnip to make the Irish and Scottish versions of 'colcannon'. The essential part, however, is that the potatoes are mashed to help soak up the gravy from the mince. Skirlie is a traditional Scottish oatmeal dish that was served with mashed potatoes and often with pheasant and grouse. Here it goes well with the mince, adding a good crunchy texture to the meal.

Mince:

450 g (1 lb) lean minced beef
2 medium onions, chopped
3 carrots, chopped
300 ml (½ pt) beef stock
1 tsp dried or 1 tbsp fresh herbs

Mashed potatoes:

1 kg (2 lb) potatoes
semi-skimmed milk
seasoning

Skirlie:

vegetable margarine
2 onions, chopped finely
1 cup oatmeal, fine or medium

Brown the mince over a gentle heat. There should be just enough fat to prevent it from sticking, but if not, add a small amount of cooking oil. If there is a lot of excess fat, however, drain this off. Add the onions and carrots and cook for 10 minutes over a low heat to soften the vegetables. Then add the herbs and stock. Leave to simmer for 20 minutes until the mince is thick and not too runny, but still has enough moisture to form a gravy. If it remains too watery, you can thicken it up by slowly adding some flour dissolved in water. Meanwhile, boil the potatoes for roughly 20 minutes or until tender. You don't have to remove the skins unless you want to. Mash them up with milk and pepper, along with any of the other ingredients you fancy from above.

To make the skirlie, melt the vegetable margarine in a pan, add the onions, and let them brown for 5 minutes. Add the oatmeal and stir well until cooked – about 10–15 minutes.

TUESDAY

• *Tomato and orange soup* •

This soup is easy to make, but you can make an even simpler version by liquidising a tin or two of tomatoes with some orange juice and heating them through. You could also leave out the orange and add mint for a change, or simply add milk to the liquidised tomatoes to give a more creamy result.

basic tomato sauce (see p. 31)

juice and rind of 2 oranges or 1 cup of orange fruit juice

Liquidise the ingredients together and warm through. Serve with a dollop of yoghurt or fromage frais.

• *Baked fish with spring onion and ginger* •

This dish has a Chinese style to it, is very simple to make and the flavours are superb. It also works very well on the barbecue cooked in tin foil parcels, and you can also use this method in the oven. Try to get good thick fillets of fish as they tend to stay more firm. You will find sesame oil in most large supermarkets, and it's worth buying for the oriental taste it adds to this dish. Serve with plain boiled rice or noodles, and a side salad or a stir-fried green vegetable.

4 fillets of white fish – cod, haddock, halibut or monkfish

3 cm (1 in.) fresh ginger, peeled and grated

6 spring onions, washed and sliced including some green

1 tbsp sesame oil (optional)

1 tbsp vegetable oil

3 tbsp soya sauce

½ tsp sugar

Pre-heat the grill and line the grill tray with foil. Rub the fish fillets on both sides with the sesame and vegetable oils. Scatter half the spring onions and ginger on to the tray and place the fish on top. Then sprinkle the remaining onion and ginger over the top. Mix the soya sauce and sugar together and spoon this over the fish as well. Pour a little water around the edges to help steam it. Place the fish under the grill and cook for 10–12 minutes or until the flesh is lightly browned on top. Be careful not to let it burn. During cooking, spoon the tray juices over the fish to baste it. To serve, remove the fillets from the tray and spoon over the pan juices, decorating them with a sprig of spring onion.

• *Caledonian ice-cream with raspberry coulis* •

This pudding tastes good served with a fruit coulis. Raspberries, strawberries, brambles and blackcurrants are all good, and if you can't get fresh ones try frozen instead. You can use tinned fruit but you will have to strain off some of the juices.

50 g (2 oz) pinhead oatmeal
2 tbsp of runny honey
450 g (1 lb) low-fat yoghurt or fromage frais
1 cup of raspberries

Brown the oatmeal by dry-frying it in a large frying-pan (see p. 9). Use a moderate heat and keep shaking the pan to stop it from burning. Cool and add the yoghurt or fromage frais along with the honey and mix well. Place the mixture in the freezer until it begins to freeze around the edges. Remove it and beat up the ice crystals that have formed. Return it to the freezer and repeat this process 1 hour later. Freeze until frozen.

Cook the raspberries over a low heat for 5 minutes and then liquidise or pulp them with a fork. Strain them through a sieve if you wish, although the slightly less smooth texture is just as good. Serve with the ice-cream.

WEDNESDAY

• *Aubergine and thyme pâté* •

This dish has a Middle Eastern influence. It is based on the same idea as hummus and is served with pitta bread or vegetable sticks. Serve it as a sandwich or baked potato filling, a starter or as a dip.

1 large aubergine
450 g (15 oz) low-fat yoghurt or fromage frais
1 tsp dried or 1 tbsp fresh thyme, chopped
juice of 1 orange
2 cloves of garlic, crushed

Prick the aubergine with a fork and bake in a pre-heated oven, 180°C (350°F) or gas mark 4, for 30 minutes or until tender. Then chop it roughly, place it in a food processor along with all the other ingredients and whiz until well blended. Pour into a bowl and chill.

• *Lemon and garlic chicken* •

This is very easy to prepare and can be left to cook in the oven with baked potatoes for Sunday dinner. Garlic is said to have medicinal properties, as well as keeping vampires away. Cooked like this it tastes sweet and wonderful – completely different from the raw stuff. Don't be put off by the amount of garlic required. The cloves can be squeezed straight from their skins and eaten with your fingers.

- **1 whole medium- sized chicken**
- **1 tbsp vegetable oil**
- **3 lemons, cut into quarters**
- **30 cloves of garlic, removed from the head, left unpeeled**
- **1 tbsp honey**
- **150 ml (¼ pt) white wine and 150 ml (¼ pt) chicken stock**

or

- **300 ml (½ pt) chicken stock**
- **1 tsp mixed dried herbs or 2 tbsp fresh herbs**
- **1 iceberg lettuce, shredded (optional)**
- **seasoning**

Pre-heat the oven to 170°C (325°F) or gas mark 3. Heat the oil in a large casserole that has a lid and will fit the whole chicken. Brown the breast side of the bird, then turn it over to brown on the other side and add pepper. Add the lemon, garlic, wine, stock, honey and herbs. Bring everything to the boil stirring occasionally, and spoon the juices over the breast. Transfer to the oven and cook for 1½ hours. If the liquid starts to reduce, as it will if the pot lid is not fitting tightly, just add some more stock or wine. Add baked potatoes to the top shelf of the oven 1 hour before the end of cooking. Test that the chicken is cooked by inserting a fork or skewer into the leg. It is cooked when the juices run clear. Remove the chicken from the casserole, place it on a heated plate and leave it to stand for 10 minutes. Then carve or divide into joints. Serve the chicken on the lettuce with the cooking juices, garlic and lemon spooned over. Eat with the baked potatoes.

THURSDAY

• *Lasagne* •

This is a meat recipe, but lasagne can be made using many different ingredients. Just follow the layering principle: first layer filling, next layer lasagne, one layer white sauce, always finishing off with a thick layer of white sauce. These days lasagne sheets do not require to be pre-cooked, but follow the instructions on the packet. For a vegetarian version, use the ratatouille recipe for the filling layer (see p. 51) or add extra vegetables such as courgettes, celery and carrots to this recipe. Serve with salad and Italian bread.

225 g (8 oz) lasagne (no pre-cooking required)
225 g (8 oz) lean mince
basic tomato sauce (see p. 31)
white sauce (see p. 44)
50 g (2 oz) cheese, grated

Pre-heat the oven to 170°C (325°F) or gas mark 3. Brown the mince over a low heat, drain off the excess fat and then add the basic tomato sauce. Heat through and, if it is very watery, reduce the mixture to the consistency of thick soup. Start by layering an oven-proof dish with one-third of the mince mixture, followed by a layer of lasagne, then a layer of white sauce. Repeat this twice more and top the last layer of white sauce with the cheese. Bake in the oven for 40 minutes until golden on top.

• *Apple and ginger cake* •

This cake does not contain any sugar and very little fat. It is sweetened using concentrated apple juice and fruit spread which are both available at health food shops. It can also be baked in a loaf-tin and eaten like a bread without the filling.

125 g (4 oz) pear and apple spread
175 g (6 oz) plain wholemeal flour
2 eggs, beaten
4 small desert apples, peeled, cored and grated
50 g (2 oz) sunflower seeds (optional)
1 tsp ground ginger
¼ tsp bicarbonate of soda
50 g (2 oz) low-fat soft cheese
1 tbsp low-fat yoghurt or fromage frais
concentrated apple juice to taste
icing sugar (optional)

Pre-heat the oven to 190°C (375°F) or gas mark 5. Mix the flour into the pear and apple spread and then add the eggs, apples, sunflower seeds, ginger and bicarbonate of soda. Beat them together and divide the mixture evenly between two 18 cm (7 in.) non-stick sponge tins and bake for 35 minutes. Cool the cakes on a wire rack. Then beat together the cheese and yoghurt or fromage frais and add some apple juice to taste. Don't add too much or the filling will become too runny. Sandwich the cakes together and dust with icing sugar if you wish.

FRIDAY

• *Bean and vegetable soup* •

This is a good soup to make when you have a tin of cooked beans in the cupboard and lots of vegetables to use up. You can use most beans, including kidney, black-eye, haricot, flageolet and chickpeas. Use any vegetables you have – the ones in the recipe are only a guideline. Serve with lots of granary bread.

1 l (2 pts) water or stock
1 tin of cooked beans (400 g/14 oz) or dried beans cooked to instruction
1 clove of garlic, crushed
1 onion, chopped
2 carrots, sliced
2 sticks of celery, sliced
2 potatoes, chopped
1 tin of tomatoes (400 g/14 oz)
1 green pepper, chopped
½ cabbage, sliced
1 courgette, sliced
1 tsp dried or 1 tbsp fresh herbs
seasoning

Simmer together the stock, beans, garlic, onion, carrot, celery, potatoes and tomatoes for 20 minutes. Add the pepper, cabbage, courgette and herbs, and cook for a further 10 minutes. Season and serve.

• *Herring in oatmeal with onion marmalade* •

Herring is inexpensive and much under-rated. It is an oil-rich fish, the type we are being encouraged to eat more often. It is good stuffed and baked. This recipe uses oatmeal to coat the fish, and it is served with a sweet-and-sour, contrasting marmalade.

4 herring, cleaned and boned
medium oatmeal, for coating
seasoning
2 tbsp vegetable oil
2 large onions (450 g/1 lb), halved and thinly sliced
50 g (2 oz) demerara sugar
2 tbsp wine or sherry vinegar
2 tbsp orange juice

In a heavy-based saucepan, gently cook the onions in half the oil for 5 minutes, stirring with a wooden spoon. Add the sugar, wine or vinegar, and orange juice, and simmer, uncovered for about 1 hour. Stir occasionally and make sure the marmalade doesn't burn. It will be dark golden and sticky when ready.

Rinse the herrings under water. Put the oatmeal on a plate and season. Coat the herrings by firmly pressing each side in the oatmeal, shaking away any loose bits. Heat the oil in a large frying-pan and fry the herrings for 5 minutes, turning once. Alternatively, bake the fish in a pre-heated oven, 180°C (350°F) or gas mark 4, for 15 minutes. Serve with the marmalade.

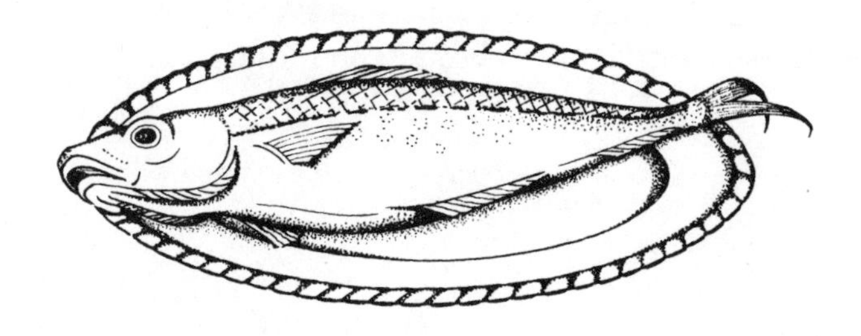

SATURDAY

• *Falafel with salsa and pitta bread* •

These are chickpea rissoles and are found in various forms all over the Middle East. They make a good starter or light meal, and can be served with a yoghurt and mint dip or tucked inside pitta bread with a crisp salad and a cold tomato salsa. You can use pre-cooked tinned chickpeas if you wish, but you will have to double the quantity to take into account the water that is absorbed during soaking.

225 g (8 oz) dried chickpeas
2 onions, finely chopped
3 tbsp parsley, chopped
2 tsp ground coriander
2 tsp ground cumin
½ tsp baking powder
4 cloves of garlic, crushed
seasoning
1 tbsp flour
vegetable oil for frying
4 pitta breads
½ iceberg lettuce, finely shredded

Soak the chickpeas in plenty of water for several hours or overnight. Drain them and rinse thoroughly. Place them in a pan with fresh cold water and bring to the boil, boiling rapidly for 10 minutes. This is important to get rid of poisonous toxins. Reduce the heat, cover and simmer for 1 hour or until tender. In a food processor, process the chickpeas to a smooth paste. Then add the onions, parsley, spices, baking powder and garlic, and process once more. Remove, knead the mixture for a moment, then let it rest in the fridge for 30 minutes. To make the falafel, take small pieces of the mixture and flatten them into little patties about 5 cm (2 in.) in diameter. If they are sticky, roll them in a little flour. Heat the oil and fry the falafel for about 2 minutes on each side over a medium heat. Drain them on kitchen paper.

• *Salsa* •

Mix all the ingredients together and serve spooned over the falafel tucked into a salad-filled pitta bread.

6 large tomatoes, skinned (or 1 tin (400 g/14 oz), drained), finely chopped
1 red onion, finely chopped
1 red or green pepper, finely chopped
1 green chilli, de-seeded and finely chopped, or a dash of Tabasco
juice of 1 lime or lemon
bunch of roughly chopped coriander

• *Gazpacho* •

This soup is Spanish in origin and is traditionally served cold. It is often best made the day before so that it has a chance to chill. However, if you are in a hurry, you can put ice cubes in the soup instead. It is lovely on a hot summer's day served with wedges of frittata, a type of omelette.

2 tins of tomatoes (400 g/14 oz each)
a good dash of Tabasco
1 red pepper, chopped
1 green pepper, chopped
½ cucumber, chopped
1 onion (preferably red), chopped
1 clove of garlic, crushed
1 tbsp wine vinegar
1 cup brown bread crumbs (optional)

Reserve some of the peppers and cucumber for the garnish. Liquidise the rest of the ingredients, apart from the breadcrumbs, and then pour them into a serving bowl. Stir through the breadcrumbs to thicken the soup, then chill and serve, garnished with the chopped vegetables.

• *Frittata* •

This is an Italian type of omelette made with potatoes. You can add whatever you have available and make up your own combinations. Leave out the ham for a vegetarian version. It is good served hot or warm, and can also be served cold. This recipe cooks the frittata on top of the cooker, but you can also do it in the oven in a baking-dish.

1 onion, sliced
1 red pepper, sliced
1 tbsp vegetable oil
2 medium potatoes, boiled and thinly sliced
6 eggs, beaten and seasoned
1 tsp dried or 1 tbsp fresh herbs
2 tomatoes, chopped
125 g (4 oz) ham, chopped
60 g (2 oz) cheddar or mozzarella cheese, grated

In a large frying-pan, gently fry the onion and the pepper in the oil over a medium heat, until the onion just starts to brown. Turn the heat down to the lowest setting and add the sliced potato in a layer. Next add the herbs to the eggs and pour them over the potatoes. Then scatter the rest of the ingredients over the top. Leave it to cook very slowly – this should take about 10–15 minutes. Don't be tempted to turn up the heat as this will burn the bottom. When all the egg has nearly set, place the frittata under a pre-heated grill to cook the top and melt the cheese. Serve cut into wedges with salad.

SUNDAY

• *Baked sardines* •

Sardines are a very tasty fish and don't need the addition of too many ingredients in their cooking. They come from the same family of fish as herring and mackerel, which all are oil-rich and very good as part of a healthy, balanced diet. Tinned sardines make an excellent snack on toast or stirred through freshly cooked pasta, but this recipe requires fresh or frozen sardines that are now available from good fishmongers. The baked sardines can be served either hot or cold with bread and a tomato and onion salad.

8 medium-sized sardines
bunch of mixed fresh herbs – parsley, chives, sage, rosemary etc.
25 g (1 oz) walnuts or almonds
2 cloves of garlic, crushed
1 tbsp olive oil
juice and rind of 1 lemon
25 g (1 oz) brown bread crumbs
freshly-ground black pepper

Pre-heat the oven to 220°C (425°F) or gas mark 7. Prepare the sardines by removing the heads, tails and fins with scissors. Slit and gut each fish and then, using the thumb, loosen the central bone from the flesh and remove, leaving the two halves still attached along the back by the skin. (Your fishmonger may do this for you.) Wash the sardines and lay half of them, skin-side down, closely together on a baking-tray greased with olive oil. Mix together the herbs, nuts, lemon rind and garlic and spread this mixture over the sardines, sprinkling them with the lemon juice. Cover each fish fillet with another sardine, skin-side up, to make a sandwich and sprinkle the bread crumbs over the top. Bake in the oven for 10 minutes, and serve with freshly-ground black pepper.

• *Yellow pea and bacon soup with blue cheese croutons* •

If you wish to make a vegetarian version of this soup leave out the bacon and use water instead of the ham stock.

170 g (6 oz) yellow split peas
1 onion, chopped
100 g (4 oz) streaky bacon, chopped
1 tbsp vegetable oil
1.5 l (3 pts) ham stock or water
1 clove of garlic, crushed
1 large carrot, chopped
1 stick of celery, chopped
1 potato, chopped
1 tsp dried or 1 tbsp fresh herbs
seasoning
2 thin slices of wholemeal bread
25 g (1 oz) stilton or any other cheese

Soak the yellow peas for at least 8 hours or overnight, and then boil them for 10 minutes in plenty of fresh water. Drain, return to the pan and add the stock. Cover and simmer for 30 minutes or until tender. Meanwhile, fry the bacon in the oil for 2 minutes and then add the rest of the vegetables, garlic and herbs, and sweat them over a low heat for 15 minutes. Add the mixture to the split peas, season and simmer for a further 30 minutes. Then place the cheese between the bread to make a sandwich, toast under a grill and cut them into 1 cm (½ in.) squares. Serve the soup hot and garnished with the croutons.

• *Teriyaki roast lamb* •

Lamb cooked this way makes a good change from traditional roast lamb. The cooking time recommended here will result in a slightly pink meat which tastes much better than if well done. The recipe uses shoulder of lamb; you can use leg, but this is more expensive. The longer you marinate the lamb, the stronger the flavours. Serve with traditional vegetables or try it with rice or warm with salad.

½ shoulder of lamb (approx. 1.5 kg/3 lb)

Marinade:

1 cup of soya sauce
3 tbsp honey
5 cloves of garlic, crushed
knob of fresh ginger (5 cm/2 in.), peeled and grated

Mix together the marinade ingredients, pour them into a holeless polythene bag and add the lamb. Leave it to marinate in the fridge for up to two days or for at least 2 hours.

Pre-heat the oven to 220°C (425°F) or gas mark 7, and place the lamb inside on a roasting-tray. Cook it for 1 hour, basting with some of the remaining marinade. Remove it from the oven and leave to rest for 20 minutes. The roasting-dish will seem quite burnt, but this is all right. Make a sauce from the remaining marinade by heating it gently over a low flame for 10 minutes or until it is the consistency you want. You can always add more honey and soya sauce if necessary. Serve this with the carved lamb.

• *Fruit brûlé* •

You can use most types of fruit in this recipe – peaches, plums, nectarines, raspberries, strawberries and bananas are all good. However, if you are using apples or gooseberries, you will have to cook them first. Don't get too hung up on quantities – they are just an approximate guide. A quick method is to add the yoghurt mixture to the fruit and simply sprinkle it with sugar before chilling it for 15 minutes and serving.

450 g (1 lb) fruit, fresh or tinned and drained

300 ml (½ pt) low-fat fromage frais

300 ml (½ pt) low-fat crême fraiche or Greek yoghurt

50 g (2 oz) soft light brown sugar

Put the fruit into a flameproof dish. Mix the fromage frais and yoghurt together and pour it over. Chill the mixture in the fridge for several hours or overnight. About 2 hours before serving, sprinkle it with the sugar. Pre-heat the grill to medium and place the brûlé underneath for a couple of minutes to caramelise the sugar. Chill again and serve.

Week 4

MONDAY

• *Red pepper soup* •

This soup is just a version of red pepper sauce (see p. 37). To serve 4–6 people, make two quantities (add some fresh basil for a change) and heat it in a saucepan. Add water to get the consistency that you want. Serve with a spoonful of fromage frais and some basil floating on top.

• *Bruschetta* •

Bruschetta is the Italian version of garlic bread. This recipe uses tomatoes as well, to make it more exciting. To make it more substantial, try adding some ham and cheese and melting it under the grill. If possible, use extra virgin oil because of its wonderful taste.

8 thick slices of white bread, cut from a crusty loaf
2 cloves of garlic, crushed
8 ripe tomatoes, chopped roughly
olive oil
freshly-ground black pepper

Grill the bread on both sides and then divide the garlic evenly between the slices, spreading it on well. Top with the tomatoes, and then drizzle over a little olive oil, grind on the pepper and serve whilst still hot.

• *Spinach and cheese cannelloni* •

This recipe uses low-fat cottage cheese but, if you can afford the extra fat and want to be truly authentic, you should use ricotta cheese. You can make a meat version of this dish using the tomato and mince filling from the lasagne recipe (see p. 61). You can buy ready-made cannelloni tubes in most large supermarkets, but you can also use rolled-up sheets of lasagne as an alternative – although this can be quite a fiddle. This makes a pleasant light meal served with a fresh green salad.

16 cannelloni tubes
450 g (1 lb) frozen spinach
350 g (12 oz) low-fat cottage cheese
freshly-grated nutmeg
freshly-ground black pepper
tomato sauce (see p. 31)

Defrost the spinach and drain it thoroughly, squeezing all the excess water away through a sieve with your hand. Mix it with the cottage cheese and add the freshly-grated nutmeg and pepper. Using a teaspoon, carefully stuff the cannelloni tubes with the mixture and place them in a single layer in a baking-dish. Cover them with the tomato sauce and bake in a pre-heated oven at 210°C (100°F) or gas mark 6 for 20 minutes or until the pasta is cooked.

TUESDAY

• *Tuna with haricot beans and tomato* •

This is a storecupboard recipe that is good in emergencies. The idea is to make sure you always have these ingredients available so that you don't have to resort to the take-away. As a starter, it can be served hot with brown bread. It can also be used as a pasta sauce or as a sandwich filling.

1 tbsp vegetable oil
1 medium onion, chopped
2 cloves of garlic, crushed
1 tin of tomatoes (400 g/14 oz), chopped
1 tin of tuna fish (225 g/8 oz), drained
1 tin of cooked haricot beans (400 g/14 oz), drained and rinsed
1 tsp dried or 1 tbsp fresh herbs
a good dash of Tabasco or 1 green chilli, chopped (optional)
seasoning

Cook the onion in the oil over a low heat for about 5 minutes. Add the garlic and chilli (optional) and cook for 5 minutes more. Add the tomatoes and their juices, the tuna fish, the beans and the herbs. Heat them thoroughly, season and serve.

• *Tarragon chicken* •

This is a simple recipe that appeals to most tastes. It can be made in advance and reheated later. It also works well with chicken joints as well as pork. Use fresh tarragon if you can get it. If not, the freeze-dried type is a good second-best.

4 chicken breasts, skinned
1 tbsp vegetable oil
1 large onion, finely chopped
2 cloves of garlic, crushed
2 tsp freeze-dried or 2 tbsp fresh tarragon, chopped
5 tbsp tomato puree
1 glass red or white wine
100 g (4 oz) button mushrooms

Heat the oil in a large frying-pan and gently brown the chicken breasts on both sides – about 10 minutes in total. Remove the chicken, add the onion and fry for 5 minutes. Then add the garlic and fry for another 2 minutes. Add half of the tarragon, the tomato puree, the wine and the mushrooms and heat them together gently. Return the chicken to the pan and leave to simmer for 10 minutes or until the chicken is cooked. If the sauce is too thin, reduce it slightly by turning up the heat. If it evaporates too quickly, add more wine or some water. Serve immediately or transfer it to a casserole to keep it warm in the oven or re-heat later.

WEDNESDAY

• *Courgette and mint soup* •

This is a wonderful soup to make at the end of the summer when courgettes are at their best. You can also try it using frozen peas or lettuce, or add a tin of tomatoes to make the soup go further. In the summer it can be served cold, and it also makes a good warming soup in the winter. Try to use fresh mint if you can, now available all year round in supermarkets.

1 tbsp vegetable oil
1 large onion, chopped
1 clove of garlic, crushed
1 potato, chopped
700 g (1½ lb) courgettes, sliced
570 ml (1 pt) stock or water
large bunch of fresh mint
freshly-ground black pepper

Heat the oil in a large saucepan and add the onion. Fry it for 3 minutes and then add the potato and garlic and cook for a further 5 minutes. Add the courgettes and stock, bring it to the boil and simmer for 20 minutes. Puree the soup in a blender and serve.

• *Salmon fishcakes with basil and tomato coulis* •

This is such a good way to eat fish and potatoes. You can use most types of fish and vary the quantities to suit your own tastes – try using half-smoked, half-unsmoked fish. You can also add lots of different herbs. Try salmon and coriander, smoked fish and parsley, tuna and tarragon, and haddock and sage. Spice them up by adding some ground cumin and coriander. Kipper and horseradish is also very good. Fishcakes really need a sauce to go with them or they can seem rather dry. Try yoghurt mixed with mint, home-made tomato sauce (see p. 31) or salsa (see p. 64). This recipe uses salmon, which is no longer the expensive fish it used to be. Ask your fishmonger to give you salmon tails and fillet ends as they should cost less.

275 g (10 oz) filleted salmon
700 g (1½ lb) potatoes, boiled and mashed
2 tbsp skimmed milk
a large bunch of fresh basil
a dash of Tabasco
freshly-ground black pepper
1 egg, beaten
flour
50 g (2 oz) breadcrumbs
1 tbsp vegetable oil for frying
½ quantity tomato sauce (see p. 31)

Poach the salmon by bringing it to the boil quickly in a pan of water. Simmer for 2 minutes, remove it from the pan and peel away the skin. Break the fish up with a fork – don't worry if it is not thoroughly cooked at this stage. Add the fish and the Tabasco to the mashed potatoes and mix them well. Set aside half the basil for the garnish and to add to the sauce. Tear up the remainder and add it to the fish mixture. If this is dry and powdery, add some milk, but not too much or it will go sticky. Place the egg, flour and breadcrumbs on three separate plates. Then divide the fish mixture into four large or eight smaller cakes, using your hands to round them off. Dip each cake, on both sides, into the flour, then the egg, the flour again, then the egg again and finally the breadcrumbs. This gives a lovely crispy coating. The cakes can either be baked on a tray in a pre-heated oven, 180°C (350°F) or gas mark 4, for 30 minutes or gently fried in the oil for 5 minutes on each side until golden brown.

To make the coulis, add the remainder of the basil to the tomato sauce, warm it through and liquidise it again. Serve the fishcakes on a plate surrounded by a pool of coulis, and decorated with a basil leaf.

• *Strawberry yoghurt ice-cream* •

This is a good way to make fruit more interesting. Other fruit purees that can be used are mango, raspberry, pineapple, banana and rhubarb. Try using honey for the sweetener instead of sugar.

225 g (8 oz) strawberries
75 g (3 oz) sugar
450 g (1 lb) low-fat natural yoghurt
1 egg white (optional)

Puree the strawberries and sugar in a blender and mix them with the yoghurt. Freeze the mixture in an ice-cream maker if you have one. If not, freeze it in a shallow container and, when the ice crystals start to form, beat and break them up with a spoon or an electric beater. Whisk the egg white until stiff and fold it into the part-frozen mixture. Return the mixture to the freezer until frozen.

THURSDAY

• *Parsnip and carrot soup* •

This soup has a lovely, smooth, velvety texture and the parsnips give it a very distinctive taste. The quantities of the vegetables used are only guidelines. If you are rather partial to parsnips, increase the quantity. For a change, try using apple in place of the carrot.

1 tbsp vegetable oil
1 onion, chopped
350 g (12 oz) parsnips, peeled and sliced
350 g (12 oz) carrots, peeled and sliced
1 potato, peeled and chopped
1 tsp curry powder
1 l (2 pts) stock or water

In a large saucepan, cook the onion in the oil for 5 minutes, add the curry powder and then the other vegetables. Heat through for 5 minutes. Add the stock and leave it to simmer for 30 minutes. Liquidise and serve.

• *Venison with mushrooms and red wine* •

Scottish venison can be either wild or farmed. You will be able to get it at most good butchers and some fishmongers also stock it. Venison is a very rich meat that is low in fat and therefore benefits from being marinated to prevent it from drying out whilst cooking. This dish can also be made with beef or lamb, and is good served with mashed potatoes and red cabbage.

2 tbsp olive oil
8 juniper berries (optional)
2 bay leaves
a bunch of fresh herbs, chopped
2 carrots, diced
1 onion, finely chopped
3 cloves of garlic, crushed
2 glasses red wine
450 g (1 lb) casserole venison (shoulder), cubed
200 g (½ lb) mushrooms
extra oil for frying
seasoning

Mix together all the above ingredients except the mushrooms and leave them to marinate for up to 2 days, or at least over night. Then strain the liquid off the meat and vegetables and put it on one side. Dry the meat and vegetables on some kitchen roll. Heat some oil in a large casserole on top of the cooker, add the meat, brown it, then add the remaining vegetable mixture and cook for 5 minutes. Pour the reserved liquid over the venison. If it does not quite cover, add some extra water. Place the casserole in a pre-heated oven, 170°C (325°F) or gas mark 3, and cook for about 1–2½ hours, stirring it every 30 minutes until the meat is done. Half an hour before serving, add the mushrooms. Season and serve piping hot.

FRIDAY

• *Spinach and nutmeg soup* •

You can use either fresh or frozen spinach in this recipe. Frozen is just as good and is probably simpler to use as it does not require to be washed and picked over. You can get ground nutmeg in a jar but for a far better, fresher taste buy whole nutmegs and grate your own on the finest edge of a grater. Use it in roughly the same quantities as you would ground pepper.

450 g (1 lb) frozen or cleaned fresh spinach
1 tbsp vegetable oil
1 onion, chopped
2 cloves of garlic, crushed
1 potato, chopped
1 l (2 pts) stock or water
freshly-grated nutmeg
seasoning
natural yoghurt for serving

Fry the onion in the olive oil and, after 5 minutes, add the nutmeg, garlic and the potato. Fry them gently for a further 5 minutes and then add the stock and cook for 20 minutes. Add the spinach, and cook for a further 5 minutes. Adjust the seasoning with a little more nutmeg if necessary, and liquidise until smooth. Serve topped with a spoonful of yoghurt and grated nutmeg.

• *Kedgeree* •

Feed this to someone who has never eaten it before and they'll love it. Really a meal on its own, but good with a salad and bread. Serve for Sunday breakfast as a change from the usual. Instead of dyed yellow haddock, go for the undyed stuff – it is more delicately flavoured.

225 g (8 oz) wholegrain rice, cooked and warm

2 large onions, chopped

1 tbsp olive oil

1 egg, hard-boiled and chopped

225 g (8 oz) smoked haddock fillet

chopped parsley for garnish

Sauce:

2 tbsp drained liquid from the cooked fish

1 tsp curry powder or paste

4 tbsp low-fat natural yoghurt

juice of 1 lemon

Fry the onion in the oil until soft but not brown. Poach the fish in just enough water to cover it, bringing it to the boil and turning off the heat. Leave it to stand for 10 minutes to flavour the water. Flake the fish and add it to the warm rice along with the onion. Make the sauce by blending the ingredients together. Pour it over and lightly toss with a fork. Garnish with the hard-boiled egg and chopped parsley.

• *Baked apples with fromage frais and pinenuts* •

Quick and simple, very tasty and kids love them.

4 large cooking apples, cored

4 tbsp raisins or sultanas

2 tbsp soft brown sugar

2 tbsp pinenuts

Pre-heat the oven to 180°C (350°F) or gas mark 4. Slit the apple skins around the middle as if making a belt. This stops them exploding during cooking. Mix the dried fruit, sugar and pinenuts together and spoon them into the core of the apples. Bake for 20 minutes in the oven, and serve with fromage frais.

SATURDAY

• *Spicy bean pâté* •

Easy to make and wonderful served with granary toast and a side salad.

1 onion, chopped
1 tbsp vegetable oil
1 clove of garlic, crushed
½ tsp ground cumin
a good dash of Tabasco (to taste)
1 tin of red kidney beans (400 g/14 oz), drained
100 ml (4 fl oz) water
2 tbsp yoghurt

Fry the onion in the oil for 10 minutes or until well browned, but not burned. Add the garlic, cumin and Tabasco sauce. Stir in the beans and water and cook for 5 minutes, mashing the beans as the mixture thickens. Add the yoghurt. Puree in a liquidiser if you want a smooth paste or leave as it is for a more chunky pâté.

• *Dahl* •

Dahl is an Indian dish based on red or yellow lentils or split peas. This recipe has used red lentils as they cook more quickly, but you can also use split peas or a mixture if you wish – but do follow the cooking instructions carefully. Dahl can be served as a side dish with other foods or as a meal in itself with rice and nan bread.

150 g (5 oz) lentils
1 cm (½ in.) fresh ginger, grated
2 tbsp vegetable oil
2 large onions, chopped
1 tsp ground turmeric
1 tsp ground cumin
1 tsp ground coriander
¼ tsp chilli powder
fresh coriander to garnish (optional)

Cover the lentils with plenty of water and cook with the ginger for 30 minutes or until soft. Meanwhile, fry the onion in the oil for about 5 minutes or until soft. Add the spices and cook for a further 3 minutes, stirring well to mix them in. Drain the lentils, add them to the onion and spices and cook together slowly for a further 10 minutes, stirring frequently to stop them from sticking. Add more water if necessary. When cooked, dahl should resemble the consistency of runny porridge.

• *Oriental pork with tomatoes, pepper and ginger* •

This recipe can also be made with lamb, beef, chicken or beans. As it is a casserole, you can use the less expensive cuts of meat that are better cooked this way. If you have any vegetables, like courgettes, broccoli, mushrooms or cabbage that need to be used up, you can add them at the same time as the pepper. If you don't like ginger, then don't use it. Try chilli powder instead.

450 g (1 lb) diced pork
1 tbsp vegetable oil
1 large onion, chopped
2 tsp root ginger, finely chopped
2 tins of tomatoes (400 g/14 oz each)
2 green peppers, in chunks
seasoning

Soften the onion in the oil over a low heat, add the ginger and lightly fry them for 1 minute. Add the pork and cook for 5 minutes, stirring to heat it evenly. Add the tomatoes, cover and cook for 1 hour over a low heat or in a pre-heated oven at 170°C (325°F) or gas mark 3. Fifteen minutes before the end of cooking, add the pepper. Serve with dahl (see p. 78), brown rice and green beans that have been cooked and seasoned with 1 tbsp soya sauce.

SUNDAY

• *Mushroom soup* •

You can add extra potato to this recipe to make it go further. The best mushrooms to use are the large open cup type as they have most flavour. Chestnut mushrooms are also good.

450 g (1 lb) mushrooms
1 onion, chopped
1 potato, chopped
1 l (2 pts) stock or water
1 tsp dried or 1 tbsp fresh parsley
½ tsp ground coriander (optional)
freshly-ground black pepper
1 tbsp fresh herbs and a little yoghurt to garnish

Place all the ingredients, apart from the herb garnish, in a saucepan and bring them to the boil. Simmer for 20 minutes, then liquidise. Serve garnished with a teaspoon of yoghurt swirled into the soup and scattered with herbs.

• *Glazed ham* •

Around Christmas and Easter time the large supermarkets often have very good offers on hams. A large ham will feed up to 20 people or can be used to feed fewer mouths and eaten cold later. Ham roasted entirely in the oven can tend to dry out. This recipe boils the ham first and finishes it off in the oven to give it a caramelised coating. The water used to boil the ham makes very good stock and can be used for making gravy.

1 ham joint
1 onion
1 bay leaf
mustard
demerara sugar
cloves

In a large pan, cover the ham with water and add the onion and bay leaf. Boil it for 30 minutes per 450 g (1 lb) and top up the pan with extra boiling water to keep the joint covered. When cooked, remove the joint from the water and strip off the rind with a knife whilst the joint is still hot. Score the fat in a criss-cross pattern and glaze by spreading it with mustard before pressing on demerara sugar. Stick a clove in each of the diamond shapes created by the scoring. Place the joint in a roasting-tin, put it into a pre-heated oven, 200°C (400°F) or gas mark 6, for 15–20 minutes and the glaze will caramelise. Set it aside for 20 minutes and carve and serve warm. Alternatively, leave it to cool completely and serve cold.

• *Cranachan* •

This is a traditional Scottish recipe that makes the best of local Scottish ingredients. Traditionally cream is used, but this version is more fat-conscious and uses a low-fat alternative.

4 tbsp medium oatmeal
300 g (10 oz) low-fat yoghurt, Greek yoghurt or fromage frais
1 tbsp runny honey
1 tbsp whisky (optional)
350 g (12 oz) fresh raspberries

Place the oatmeal in a non-stick frying-pan and stir over a low heat until lightly toasted. Remove from the heat and cool completely. Drain any excess liquid from the top of the yoghurt and add the honey and whisky (optional). Fold half of the cooled oatmeal into the mixture and keep the rest for sprinkling on the top. Layer the raspberries and yoghurt evenly between four glasses, making 2–3 layers of each. Refrigerate for 2 hours and serve sprinkled with the remaining oats.

Index

Printed in Scotland for The Stationery Office Limited by CC No. 3093 30C 4/97.